# BIBLE BRAINSTORMS

ROGER HOWERTON

Word Games & Puzzles from the Gospels

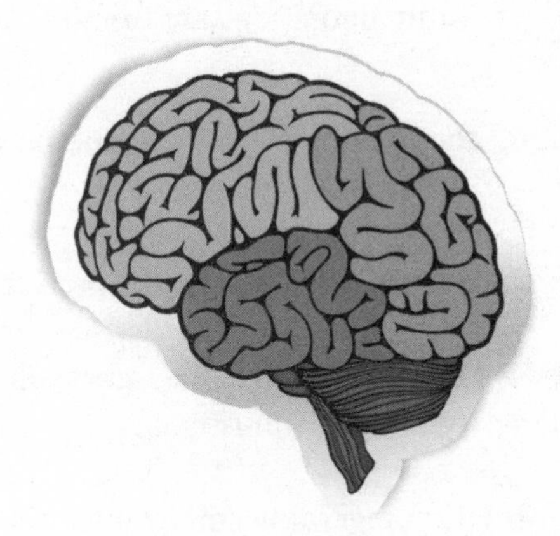

First printing: November 2014
Second printing: May 2019



New Leaf Press, P.O. Box 726, Green Forest, AR 72638

New Leaf Press is a division of the New Leaf Publishing Group, Inc.

ISBN: 978-0-89221-725-0
ISBN: 978-1-61458-693-7 (digital)

Cover by Diana Bogardus

Unless otherwise noted, Scripture quotations are from the King James Version of the Bible.

Please consider requesting that a copy of this volume be purchased by your local library system.

**Printed in the United States of America**

## TABLE OF CONTENTS

# THE GOSPEL ACCORDING TO ST. MATTHEW

## JESUS' GENEALOGY

*See if you can name each of the 12 people described below. All of them are listed in the genealogy of Jesus in Matthew 1.*

1. She is the only woman in the list with a book of the Bible named for her. ________
2. His name was changed to Israel. ________
3. This king played the harp. ________
4. In faith, she hung a scarlet thread out of her window. ________
5. This king died of a disease in his feet. ________
6. God made him "father of many nations." ________
7. He is listed as "the husband of Mary." ________
8. When he was born, his father was 100 years old. ________
9. He sealed a deal with a shoe in order to marry Ruth. ________
10. He fathered eight sons; the youngest became a great king. ________
11. He had 700 wives. ________
12. He was governor in charge of rebuilding Solomon's temple. ________

## 2 ADD-A-LETTER 1

*Begin with the letter shown, then add one letter at each step, rearranging the letters each time to fit the definition at the right. The last answer will be a key word from the book of Matthew.*

| | | | | | | | |
|---|---|---|---|---|---|---|---|
| | E | | | | | | |
| Myself | | | | | | | |
| Encountered | | | | | | | |
| Abound | | | | | | | |
| Gauge | | | | | | | |
| Irritability | | | | | | | |
| Satan (in the wilderness) | | | | | | | |

## 3 CAN YOU FOLLOW DIRECTIONS?

*Start with the phrase "Joseph laid the body in his own tomb" at the top and follow the directions, step-by-step. Keep the letters in order at each step, making only the change requested. The final answer will be a phrase from the book of Matthew that is related to the beginning phrase.*

1. Reverse the letters in the words "laid," "body," and "tomb."
2. Reverse the letters in "Joseph," and move the result to the end.
3. Remove the plural pronoun, the flying insect, and the foreign currency.
4. Change every D to an S.
5. After the third letter, add the word "sirs."
6. Replace every L and J with "ieh."
7. Replace the word that means "cry" with the word "of."
8. Replace the word that means "possess" with the word "ton."
9. Change every B to an S.
10. Remove the first three letters.
11. Replace "in his" with the three-letter poetic word for "before."
12. Place an R after the first H.
13. Place an H between the words "ere" and "ton."
14. Place the letters N and E at the beginning.
15. Reverse the string of letters.

JOSEPHLAIDTHEBODYINHISOWNTOMB

1. ______________________________
2. ______________________________
3. ______________________________
4. ______________________________
5. ______________________________
6. ______________________________
7. ______________________________
8. ______________________________
9. ______________________________
10. ______________________________
11. ______________________________
12. ______________________________
13. ______________________________
14. ______________________________
15. ______________________________

## 4 KNOCKOUTS

*Below is a quotation of Jesus from the book of Matthew. All of the words are there, in the correct order, with the letters in correct order as well, but one letter has been added to each word. "Knock out" the unnecessary letter in each word to reveal the quotation.*

FORM THEE SOON OFT MEAN HIS COMES
TWO SALVE THATS WHITCH WASH LOIST.

________________________________________________

________________________________________________

## 5 THE PARABLE OF THE SOWER (HOMONYMS, SYNONYMS, ANTONYMS)

*Below is the parable of the sower from Matthew 13. Many blanks have been left in the story, with a word in parentheses before each blank. That word is a homonym (same sound, different spelling), a synonym (same meaning), or an antonym (opposite) of the correct answer for the blank. Figure out the correct answers to properly complete the story.*

A (planter) ________________ went (in) ________________ to (sew) ________________, and as he sowed, some seeds fell (buy) ________________ the roadside, and the (fowls) ________________ came and devoured them. Others fell (off) ________________ (stony) ________________ ground, where they didn't have much (dirt) ________________, and immediately they sprang (down) ________________, because they had (know) ________________ depth of earth. When the (son) ________________ had (sunk) ________________, they were scorched. Because they had no (route) ________________, they withered away. Others (dropped) ________________ among thorns. The thorns (shrank) ________________ up and choked them. Others fell on (bad) ________________ soil, and yielded fruit: (sum) ________________ one hundred (thymes) ________________ as much, some sixty, and some thirty.

## 6 MOVIN' UP 1

*Move the letters in each column up and into the boxes above (not necessarily in the order the letters are in now) to find a quote from Jesus in the book of Matthew. A block signifies the end of a word.*

| | | | | | | | | | | | | | | | | | | | |
|---|---|---|---|---|---|---|---|---|---|---|---|---|---|---|---|---|---|---|---|
| | | | | ■ | | | ■ | | | | ■ | | | | | | | | |
| | | | | ■ | | | ■ | | | ■ | | | | | | | ■ | | |
| | ■ | | | | ■ | | ■ | | | | | ■ | | | | | | ■ | |
| | | | | ■ | | | ■ | | | | | | | ■ | | | | | |
| ■ | | | | | | | ■ | | | | | ■ | | | | | | | ■ |

| | | | | | | | | | | | | | | | | | | | |
|---|---|---|---|---|---|---|---|---|---|---|---|---|---|---|---|---|---|---|---|
| D | E | A | H | A | I | D | A | I | E | C | E | E | A | H | E | E | A | A | L |
| E | I | C | H | Y | I | F | | S | H | E | R | E | C | P | E | C | H | L | N |
| H | R | E | H | | T | N | | T | H | E | R | F | O | R | H | H | L | Y | S |
| P | R | T | W | | R | O | | T | H | Y | S | | T | T | I | N | R | | W |
| | | T | Y | | | S | | T | N | | | | W | | S | T | | | |

## 7 THE WORD WITHIN

*Fill in the blanks with words that answer each clue. The words will be of varying lengths. When read top to bottom, the completed words will reveal a quotation from the book of Matthew.*

| | | |
|---|---|---|
| 1. | Not more | B____________ED |
| 2. | 2nd tone of musical scale | A____________ |
| 3. | Not she | T____________ |
| 4. | Exclamation upon seeing a mouse | M____________ |
| 5. | Either | F____________ |
| 6. | Attention getter | T____________ |
| 7. | Corridor | S____________ |
| 8. | Feminine pronoun | IN____________IT |
| 9. | Ordinal follower of 4 or 7 | ____________E |
| 10. | Rembrandt's line of work | E____________H |

## CHANGE-A-LETTER

*Change one letter in every word below to make another word. When finished, a quotation of Jesus will be revealed.*

LEAVEN AID GARTH SHELL PAST SWAY,
BAT BY WORKS STALL NOW PANS AWRY.

______________________________________________

______________________________________________

## 9 LEFTOVERS

*Answer the quiz questions below. The answers may be found in the list of words, though not necessarily in order. Cross off each answer from the list. The remaining words, when read left to right, top to bottom, will reveal a quotation from the book of Matthew. Scripture references have been given at the end of each question.*

| No | Three | Servants | Hate |
|---|---|---|---|
| Money | Man | Yes | Woman |
| Can | Serve | Disciples | Two |
| Teach | Love | Masters | Wedding |

1. What gender of person had the issue of blood? (9:20) ______________
2. Jesus said, "Do good to them that ______________ you." (5:44)
3. For what event were servants sent out to look for guests? (22:10) ______________
4. How many measures of meal did the woman hide leaven in? (13:33) ______________
5. What did Peter find in the mouth of a fish? (17:27) ______________
6. Jesus said, "Thou shalt ______________ thy neighbor...." (19:19)
7. Did Mary Magdalene visit the tomb of Jesus? (27:61) ______________
8. To whom did Herod tell that John the Baptist had risen from the dead? (14:2) ______________
9. Jesus said to go and ______________ all nations. (28:19)
10. Whom did the soldiers say had stolen the body of Jesus? (28:13) ______________

## 10 VANITY PLATES

*Of course, there were no automobiles in Bible times, and certainly no license plates. But let's assume for a moment that the chariots had to have license plates. Can you match the personalized license plate to the person in the book of Matthew who would have displayed it?*

| | |
|---|---|
| 1. WTRWLKR | A. Judas Iscariot |
| 2. CARPNTR | B. Caiaphas |
| 3. ROMNGOV | C. John the Baptist |
| 4. TAXMAN | D. Joseph (Jesus' father) |
| 5. BAPTIZR | E. Herod the tetrarch |
| 6. LEAD100 | F. Simon Peter |
| 7. 30SILVR | G. Matthew |
| 8. VRGNMOM | H. Centurion |
| 9. HI – PRST | I. Mary (Jesus' mother) |
| 10. BDAYBOY | J. Pontius Pilate |

## ONE OR THE OTHER

*Cross out one letter in each box so that the remaining letters will spell out a quotation from the book of Matthew. A black box signifies the end of a word.*

| | | | | | | | |
|---|---|---|---|---|---|---|---|
| G L | O I | V F | T E | ■ | I U | S P | ■ |
| T S | P H | A I | S N | ■ | D P | I A | Y N |
| ■ | T O | U W | R O | ■ | S D | A H | I A |
| S L | T Y | ■ | T B | H R | E I | N A | D E |

__________________________________________

__________________________________________

## 12 CROSSROADS

*Each crossroad below contains two words that make a phrase from the book of Matthew. Fill in the blanks from the word list below. The first word of each grid should be placed down, and the second word across.*

| | | | |
|---|---|---|---|
| Beloved | Daily | Loaves | Prophet |
| Blind | False | Man | Son |
| Bread | Five | Men | Wicked |
| Come | Kingdom | One | Wise |

1

2

3

4

5

6

7

8

## 13 LOST SHEEP

*In Matthew 18, Jesus spoke of a man who had a hundred sheep, but one had gone astray. Can you help find it? In the puzzle below, the word "sheep" appears only once. The word may be forward, backward, diagonal, vertical or horizontal. Find it.*

| S | E | P | E | E | S | H | P | S | S | E | E | H | S | P | H | S | E | E | E |
|---|---|---|---|---|---|---|---|---|---|---|---|---|---|---|---|---|---|---|---|
| P | H | E | E | S | H | E | E | S | P | S | E | H | E | E | S | P | H | P | E |
| E | S | P | P | H | E | E | P | H | E | E | P | E | E | S | H | E | E | E | P |
| E | E | H | S | H | P | S | S | E | E | H | P | E | P | E | E | E | H | S | E |
| P | E | S | E | E | P | H | E | S | E | E | H | P | S | P | E | H | E | E | S |
| E | P | E | P | S | E | E | E | P | H | S | E | S | E | E | S | P | H | H | P |
| S | E | P | E | E | S | H | P | S | S | E | E | H | S | P | H | S | E | E | E |
| S | S | E | H | H | E | E | P | H | E | E | P | E | E | S | H | E | E | E | P |
| H | P | S | H | E | S | E | S | H | P | P | E | E | E | E | H | E | E | P | S |
| E | E | P | S | H | E | P | H | E | E | S | H | S | H | E | P | E | S | H | E |
| P | H | E | E | S | H | E | E | S | P | E | E | H | E | E | S | P | H | P | E |
| H | S | E | E | P | E | P | H | P | E | E | S | H | S | H | E | E | H | E | P |
| E | E | S | H | S | E | H | E | E | S | S | P | E | H | E | P | E | S | S | E |
| E | S | E | P | H | E | E | P | H | E | E | P | E | E | S | H | E | E | E | P |
| P | E | H | S | E | P | S | H | E | E | E | S | H | E | P | P | H | H | E | P |
| S | H | E | P | E | S | E | E | P | H | P | E | E | S | H | E | P | E | E | S |
| S | E | P | E | S | S | E | P | H | E | E | P | H | E | E | P | E | E | S | H |
| H | E | H | P | E | H | S | E | P | S | H | E | E | E | S | H | E | P | P | H |
| E | S | H | S | H | P | S | S | E | E | H | P | E | P | E | E | E | H | S | E |
| P | E | H | S | E | S | H | P | S | S | E | E | H | S | P | H | S | E | E | E |

## 14 IT'S A LIVING

*The list below consists of occupations from the book of Matthew in code—one letter stands for another. Each code letter represents the same letter throughout the list. When you have identified a word in the list, use the solved letters to help decode the other words. For example, KDBBDF could be LETTER.*

F Y G W L B T G W I O

__________ ____________

B Y V T G I W W

________________

H W T F Y V Z O

________________

M G Z Q

________

L G I Y W T H V Z

__________________

I V A A J F W W

________________

I W T C V Z O

______________

B T S B Y W O

______________

B J K X G F V Z

________________

Y J I K V Z A H V Z

____________________

## 15 MATTHEW'S CHRISTMAS QUIZ

*Matthew tells much about the birth of Christ, and so does Luke. Putting these two accounts together gives us the bulk of what we know about the event. See if you can answer the questions below from the book of Matthew. Place the letter of each correct answer in order to reveal a related Christmas phrase.*

1. In what city was Jesus born?
   f. Jerusalem g. Bethlehem h. Nazareth
2. What was the name of the king of Judaea at the time?
   o. Herod p. Pontius Pilate q. Nero
3. From what direction did the wise men come?
   d. east e. west f. north
4. To what city did the wise men come?
   w. Jerusalem x. Bethlehem y. Nazareth
5. What did Herod ask the chief priests and scribes?
   h. what time the wise men arrived
   i. where Christ was to be born
   j. what time the star appeared
6. What did Herod ask the wise men?
   r. what time the wise men arrived
   s. where Christ was to be born
   t. what time the star appeared
7. What gifts did the wise men bring to Jesus?
   h. myrrh, frankincense, and gold
   i. gold, silver, and frankincense
   j. frankincense, gold, and figs
8. Why didn't the wise men return to Herod?
   s. Herod told them never to return
   t. they lost their way
   u. God warned them not to return
9. Who warned Joseph to flee with his family to Egypt?
   r. Herod s. angel of the Lord t. wise men

________________________________________

________________________________________

## 16 WORD LADDER 1

*Each ladder has five columns. Every answer in column A will have five letters; every answer in column B will have four; answers in column C will have three. After answering the definition for A1, one letter can be dropped and the remaining four letters rearranged to make the answer for B1. Place the dropped letter into the box to the left of column A. Drop another letter from the B1 answer and rearrange the remaining three letters to form the answer for C1. Place the dropped letter into the box to the right of column C. Continue this pattern for the entire puzzle. When finished, the columns of dropped letters, reading down, will reveal a phrase from the book of Matthew.*

| | | A | | | | | B | | | | C | | | |
|---|---|---|---|---|---|---|---|---|---|---|---|---|---|---|
| 1 | | | | | | | | | | | | | | |
| 2 | | | | | | | | | | | | | | |
| 3 | | | | | | | | | | | | | | |
| 4 | | | | | | | | | | | | | | |
| 5 | | | | | | | | | | | | | | |

A1. Short trip
A2. Stock market unit
A3. One killed Goliath
A4. Reason
A5. Speed

B1. Fish for salad
B2. Skin irritation
B3. Notice
B4. Attorney's project
B5. Despise

C1. Acorn or pecan
C2. Possesses
C3. Number of lepers healed
C4. Top card
C5. Derby, for one

## 17 MOVIN' UP 2

*Move the letters in each column up and into the boxes above (not necessarily in the order the letters are in now) to find a quote from Jesus in the book of Matthew. A block signifies the end of a word.*

| | | | | | | | | | | |
|---|---|---|---|---|---|---|---|---|---|---|
| | ■ | | | | | ■ | | | | |
| ■ | | | ■ | | | | ■ | | | ■ |
| | ■ | | | | | ■ | | | | |
| | | ■ | | | ■ | | | | ■ | ■ |
| A | I | C | B | E | E | H | C | A | A | N |
| A | T | H | I | L | L | T | I | D | N | T |
| O | | S | I | S | Y | | T | H | N | |
| | | | | T | | | | O | | |

## 18 EARLY LIFE OF CHRIST

*All of the words hidden in this puzzle are from the second chapter of Matthew, which recounts the birth and early years of the life of Christ. Search for the words forward, backward, vertically, horizontally, and diagonally.*

| | | |
|---|---|---|
| Angel | Gold | Prophet |
| Bethlehem | Governor | Scribes |
| Chief priests | Herod | Sleep |
| Dream | Joy | Son |
| East | King | Star |
| Egypt | Mary | Virgin |
| Emmanuel | Myrrh | Wife |
| Frankincense | Name | Wise men |

```
S U E R P S O T P Y G E
L T D U S E B I R C S M
E R S L O N E A O N Y M
G O N E O I M L E A O A
N G R E I G H C S M J N
A T N F E R N M T E H U
D E S I N I P S A R X E
O H R W K V A F R E N L
R P O N I E J Y E O R Z
E O A T N E M E S I W D
H R O N R E V O G Q H O
F P B E T H L E H E M C
```

## 19 WHERE AM I?

*Put together a set of letters in column A with a set in columns B and C to form the name of a place from the book of Matthew. Use each set only once. No rearranging of letters is necessary to form the words.*

| | Column A | Column B | Column C | |
|---|---|---|---|---|
| 1. | BETH | A | ALEM | ______________________ |
| 2. | BETH | A | AN | ______________________ |
| 3. | BETH | A | CHO | ______________________ |
| 4. | CAN | DER | DA | ______________________ |
| 5. | CAP | E | EL | ______________________ |
| 6. | EG | ER | HEM | ______________________ |
| 7. | GAL | I | LEE | ______________________ |
| 8. | GETH | I | MANE | ______________________ |
| 9. | IS | LE | NAUM | ______________________ |
| 10. | JER | RA | NESS | ______________________ |
| 11. | JER | SAI | NY | ______________________ |
| 12. | NAZ | SE | PT | ______________________ |
| 13. | NIN | US | RETH | ______________________ |
| 14. | WIL | Y | VEH | ______________________ |

## 20 WORD LADDER 2

*Each ladder has five columns. Every answer in column A will have five letters; every answer in column B will have four; answers in column C will have three. After answering the definition for A1, one letter can be dropped and the remaining four letters rearranged to make the answer for B1. Place the dropped letter into the box to the left of column A. Drop another letter from the B1 answer and rearrange the remaining three letters to form the answer for C1. Place the dropped letter into the box to the right of column C. Continue this pattern for the entire puzzle. When finished, the columns of dropped letters, reading down, will reveal a phrase from the book of Matthew.*

| | | A | | | | | B | | | | C | | | |
|---|---|---|---|---|---|---|---|---|---|---|---|---|---|---|
| 1 | | | | | | | | | | | | | | |
| 2 | | | | | | | | | | | | | | |
| 3 | | | | | | | | | | | | | | |
| 4 | | | | | | | | | | | | | | |
| 5 | | | | | | | | | | | | | | |
| 6 | | | | | | | | | | | | | | |
| 7 | | | | | | | | | | | | | | |

A1. Sneaker accessories
A2. Moses' brother
A3. Devil
A4. Jesus turned it to wine
A5. Intended
A6. Smallest
A7. Recognized

B1. Perfect serves
B2. Horse color
B3. Finished
B4. A frog may have one
B5. Tidy
B6. Archealogical sites
B7. Understand

C1. Red or North
C2. Neither's partner
C3. Bambi's mom
C4. Mr. Linkletter
C5. Butterfly catcher
C6. Matching group
C7. Finished first

## 21 MATTHEW'S FAMILIAR PHRASES

*The list below consists of familiar phrases from the book of Matthew in code—one letter stands for another. Each code letter represents the same letter throughout the list. When you have identified a word in the list, use the solved letters to help decode the other words. For example, KDBBDF could be LETTER. (If you need help getting started, a hint is given below the puzzle.)*

Q K F O   X E P F O B   P I Z   C Y E   Q K B W O B

C W O   B P X C   E Q   C W O   O P H C W

J P I R   L P X X O Z   A V C   Q O Y   L W E B O I

P I   O R O   Q E H   P I   O R O

A X O B B O Z   P H O   C W O   J O O S

C W O   X K M W C   E Q   C W O   Y E H X Z

H P K I   E I   C W O   N V B C   P I Z   C W O   V I N V B C

Y O O D K I M   P I Z   M I P B W K I M   E Q   C O O C W

P   L K C R   B O C   E I   P   W K X X

Starting hint: C = T

## 22 FAMOUS PEOPLE WITH BIBLE NAMES

*Fill in the blank with a name from the book of Matthew to complete the famous names.*

1. *Frankenstein* Author ____________________ Shelley
2. *The Hobbit* Director ____________________ Jackson
3. "Burnin' Up" Singers ____________________ Brothers
4. Former Broncos Quarterback ____________________ Elway
5. "You Can Call Me Al" Singer Paul ____________________
6. First First Lady ____________________ Washington
7. *Inception* Actor ____________________ Gordon-Levitt
8. Painter ____________________ Gainsborough
9. Industrialist ____________________ Carnegie
10. *Your Show of Shows* Comedian Sid ____________________
11. Soccer Player ____________________ Beckham
12. Western Outlaw ____________________ ____________________

## 23 MOVIN' UP 3

*Move the letters in each column up and into the boxes above (not necessarily in the order the letters are in now) to find a quote from Jesus in the book of Matthew. A block signifies the end of a word.*

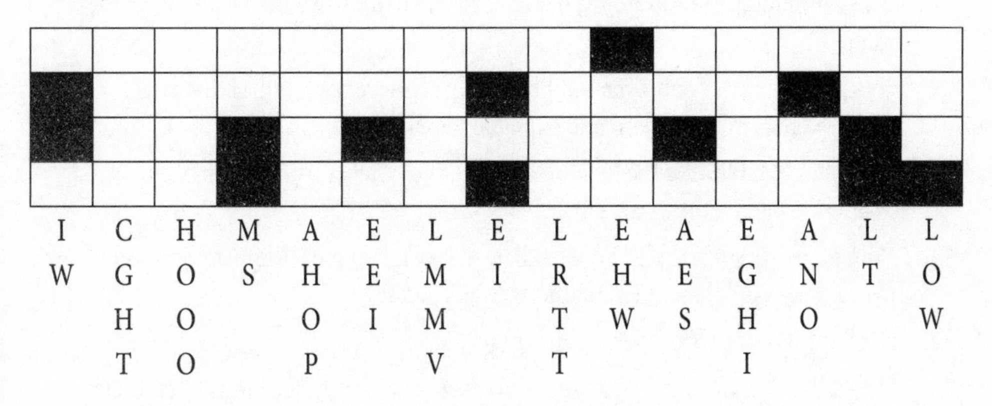

## 24 WORD OF MOUTH

*These quotations are not from the Bible, but if a reporter had been on the scene to get a scoop, he or she may have included them in the story. See if you can identify the person from the book of Matthew who might have said each one. A list of names is given from which to choose.*

| | | |
|---|---|---|
| _____ Herod | _____ John the Baptist | _____ Peter |
| _____ Herodias | _____ Joseph of Arimathaea | _____ Judas |
| _____ James | _____ Peter's mother-in-law | _____ Pontius Pilate |
| _____ John | _____ Simon of Cyrene | _____ Mary |
| _____ Joseph | _____ Woman with blood disease | _____ Matthew |

1. "You see, my daughter was a very good dancer."
2. "The kiss? It meant nothing. It was simply a way to identify Him to the mob."
3. "Naturally, I was suspicious when I found out that she was going to have a baby."
4. "After 12 years of suffering, I was desperate to try anything, and all I could reach was His clothing."
5. "When I heard that rooster crow, I realized what I had done, and was so very sorry."
6. "You won't believe me, but I felt so good after Jesus healed me that I jumped out of bed and fixed dinner for everyone!"
7. "Actually, locusts taste just like chicken!"
8. "I never thought He was guilty, but of course, I had to give the people what they wanted."
9. "I explained it over and over, but he wouldn't believe me … until that angel appeared to him in a dream and explained it all."
10. "You should have seen the look on the other guys' faces when Mother requested that James and I sit next to Jesus."
11. "You bet I was surprised! Those soldiers just grabbed me—Me! An innocent bystander!—and demanded that I carry His cross!"
12. "Collecting taxes was never my dream job, anyway."
13. "I told those smart-aleck wise guys to report back to me, but I never saw them again."
14. "It was definitely the voice of God, and Peter and John heard it, too!"
15. "I certainly didn't need the tomb for myself—it was the least I could do."

## PARABLES, PARABLES

*Matthew records many parables of Jesus. Using the word list below, fill in the blanks to make a correct statement.*

| City | Earth | Enemy | Field |
|---|---|---|---|
| Fowls | Highways | Inheritance | Net |
| Oil | Sun | Vineyard | Garment |

1. ______________ devoured the seeds that fell by the wayside (13:4).
2. The man at the wedding was bound and cast out because he didn't have the proper ______________ (22:11).
3. The five virgins who were called foolish had no ______________ with them (25:3).
4. The ______________ sowed tares among the wheat (13:25).
5. A man told his two sons to work in his ______________ (21:28).
6. When the guests would not come to the wedding, and killed the king's messengers, the king burned their ______________ (22:7).
7. The ______________ caused the plants in the stony places to wither away (13:6).
8. When the man found the hidden treasure, he sold all he had to buy the ______________ (13:44).
9. The man who was only given one talent hid it in the ______________ (25:25).
10. When the man who built the vineyard sent his son to collect fruit from the keepers, they killed him so they could take his ______________ (25:38).
11. The kingdom of heaven is like a ______________ that was cast in the sea (13:47).
12. When no guests would come to the wedding, the king sent his servants into the ______________ to find anyone who would come (22:9).

## WORD TRIANGLES

*Each of the triangles below is an anagram of a 10-letter word found within the book of Matthew. There are no proper nouns or plurals. Unscramble each word.*

| 1. | 2. | 3. |
|---|---|---|
| E | A | B |
| E G | C E | E I |
| I N N | E E N | D G O |
| O T R A | N P R T | M R O R |
| ________ | ________ | ________ |

| 4. | 5. | 6. |
|---|---|---|
| A | C | B |
| E I | A I | B B |
| M O N | M N O | E E I |
| P T T T | O S S P | N I W R |
| ________ | ________ | ________ |

| 7. | 8. | 9. |
|---|---|---|
| S | A | B |
| S E | D D | E I |
| E R N | E R N | O S S |
| W D I L | S U N T | O T R U |
| ________ | ________ | ________ |

## 27 WRITER'S BLOCKS

*Matthew mentions many people by their occupation as he tells the story of Christ. In each row of blocks below is the name of one of these groups, but the name has been divided into blocks of three letters or less and mixed up. The letters within each block are in order, but the blocks are not. Oh, and an extra block of letters has been added for fun. Take away the unneeded block and put the others in order to find 10 occupations.*

| | | | | | |
|---|---|---|---|---|---|
| CEE | TER | DU | SAD | | ________ |
| PHA | EE | BLE | RIS | | ________ |
| DI | ER | SOL | NDL | | ________ |
| TUR | RES | CEN | ION | | ________ |
| OR | PHE | SHE | RD | | ________ |
| MAN | FIS | SO | HER | | ________ |
| NST | MI | PP | REL | | ________ |
| MON | EYC | OUT | HAN | GER | ________ |
| LIC | PUB | ER | AN | | ________ |
| VER | TI | GO | NOR | | ________ |

## 28 ADD-A-LETTER 2

*Begin with the letter shown, then add one letter at each step, rearranging the letters each time to fit the definition at the right. The last answer will be a key word from the book of Matthew.*

| | | | | | | | |
|---|---|---|---|---|---|---|---|
| | A | | | | | | |
| A preposition | | | | | | | |
| Greek letter | | | | | | | |
| Price | | | | | | | |
| Fall flower | | | | | | | |
| Withhold food | | | | | | | |
| The "greatest among you" | | | | | | | |

## 29 THE TWELVE

*The list below consists of the disciples, as Matthew named them, in code—one letter stands for another. Each code letter represents the same letter throughout the list. When you have identified a word in the list, use the solved letters to help decode the other words. For example, KDBBDF could be LETTER.*

T A R Y Z  S F D F C

__________ __________

P Z N C F J

____________

I P R F T,  D B F  T Y Z  Y M  O F V F N F F

__________ ______ ______ ____ ______________

I Y B Z

________

S B A K A S

____________

V P C D B Y K Y R F J

______________________

D B Y R P T

____________

R P D D B F J

______________

I P R F T,  D B F  T Y Z  Y M  P K S B P F H T

__________ ______ ______ ____ ________________

D B P N N P F H T

__________________

T A R Y Z  D B F  W P Z P P Z A D F

__________ ______ __________________

I H N P T  A T W P C A Y D

__________ ________________

## 30 A PROCESS OF ELIMINATION

*Follow the directions below, eliminating items from the word list. When the correct items have been removed, the remaining words, reading left to right, top to bottom, will reveal a quotation from the book of Matthew.*

1. Delete all prime numbers.
2. Delete all words with double letters.
3. Delete all synonyms for *small*.
4. Delete all names of cities.
5. Delete all animals, including birds.
6. Delete all professional baseball mascots.
7. Delete all words with a silent first letter.
8. Delete all words that can combine with *sun* to make a compound word.
9. Delete all words that rhyme with *wheel*.

| | | |
|---|---|---|
| Foxes | Little | Great |
| One | Falls | Dove |
| Heal | Light | Tiny |
| Nazareth | Is | Angels |
| Shall | Bear | Your |
| Street | Shine | Slight |
| Three | Steal | Giants |
| Know | Eagle | Capernaum |
| Reward | Two | In |
| Will | Kill | Gnat |
| Jerusalem | Heaven | Rise |

______________________________________________

______________________________________________

## 31 WORD LADDER 3

*Each ladder has five columns. Every answer in column A will have five letters; every answer in column B will have four; answers in column C will have three. After answering the definition for A1, one letter can be dropped and the remaining four letters rearranged to make the answer for B1. Place the dropped letter into the box to the left of column A. Drop another letter from the B1 answer and rearrange the remaining three letters to form the answer for C1. Place the dropped letter into the box to the right of column C. Continue this pattern for the entire puzzle. When finished, the columns of dropped letters, reading down, will reveal a phrase from the book of Matthew.*

| | | A | | | | | | B | | | | C | | |
|---|---|---|---|---|---|---|---|---|---|---|---|---|---|---|
| 1 | | | | | | | | | | | | | | |
| 2 | | | | | | | | | | | | | | |
| 3 | | | | | | | | | | | | | | |
| 4 | | | | | | | | | | | | | | |
| 5 | | | | | | | | | | | | | | |
| 6 | | | | | | | | | | | | | | |

A1. Hook
A2. Tantalize
A3. Doll material
A4. Arm joint
A5. Majestic
A6. Attacks

B1. Short visit
B2. Chair
B3. Harvest
B4. Fido's dish
B5. Strong wind
B6. Dry

C1. Tabby
C2. Rested
C3. One of a certain set
C4. Hair decoration
C5. Fall behind
C6. Lighter than _____

## 32 SCAVENGER HUNT

*Can you find:*

1. A ruminant in Matthew 19:24 ______________________
2. A unit of length in Matthew 4:6 ______________________
3. Pages in a book in Matthew 24:32 ______________________
4. A layer of paint in Matthew 5:40 ______________________
5. A court separator in Matthew 13:47 ______________________
6. A season in Matthew 7:27 ______________________
7. A multiplication chart in Matthew 15:27 ______________________
8. Playing cards in Matthew 10:18 ______________________
9. A suit in Matthew 18:35 ______________________
10. A foot finder in Matthew 24:47 ______________________
11. A car in Matthew 14:11 ______________________
12. Two halves in Matthew 9:22 ______________________

## 33 ADD-A-LETTER 3

*Begin with the letter shown, then add one letter at each step, rearranging the letters each time to fit the definition at the right. The last answer will be a key word from the book of Matthew.*

| | | | | | | |
|---|---|---|---|---|---|---|
| | E | | | | | |
| Second note of singing scale | | | | | | |
| Each | | | | | | |
| Lively | | | | | | |
| Two books are named for him | | | | | | |
| John the Baptist imperative | | | | | | |

## 34 RED-LETTER EDITION

*Each answer below is the word that fills in the blank to complete the phrase in the clue. All of the phrases are from sayings of Jesus in the book of Matthew. When each answer is correctly filled in, the shaded boxes, reading down, will reveal a quotation of Jesus that fits the theme of this puzzle. The Scripture reference from Matthew for each clue is given in parentheses.*

A grain of ___ seed (13:31)
This is my ___ (26:26)
It is ___ to do well (12:12)
Abomination of ___ (24:15)
The right hand of ___ (26:64)
___ not that ye be not judged (7:1)
I am not come to ___ (5:17)
Where your ___ is (6:21)
Thy ___ hath made thee whole (9:22)
___ all nations (28:19)
The poor have the ___ preached (11:5)
For many are ___ (22:14)
The ___ of heaven (13:44)
My ___ is easy (11:30)
Some fell among ___ (13:7)
A ___ is not without honour (13:57)
Man shall not live by ___ alone (4:4)
The ___ have holes (8:20)
___ as doves (10:16)
Revealed them unto ___ (11:25)
Five of them were ___ (25:2)
Seek and ye ___ find (7:7)
Give us this ___ our daily bread (6:11)

______________________________________

______________________________________

## 35 FAMILY TREE

*See how many people you can find from Jesus' genealogy in Matthew. The names can read forward, backward, up, down, or diagonally. When all answers have been found, the 23 leftover letters, when read left to right, top to bottom, will reveal a related phrase.*

| | | |
|---|---|---|
| Abijah | Jechoniah | Obed |
| Abraham | Jehoshaphat | Rahab |
| Ahaz | Jesse | Rehoboam |
| Amon | Joram | Ruth |
| Asa | Joseph | Sadoc |
| Azor | Josiah | Salmon |
| Boaz | Jotham | Solomon |
| David | Judah | Tamar |
| Eleazar | Manasseh | Uriah |
| Isaac | Mary | Uzziah |
| Jacob | Matthan | Zerubbabel |

| | | | | | | | | | | | | |
|---|---|---|---|---|---|---|---|---|---|---|---|---|
| Z | H | A | D | U | J | O | T | H | A | M | J | M |
| A | P | J | E | C | H | O | N | I | A | H | A | A |
| H | E | E | B | A | H | A | R | S | U | T | S | N |
| A | S | E | S | Y | R | A | M | A | T | A | R | A |
| S | O | L | O | M | O | N | W | H | M | A | U | S |
| S | J | E | H | O | S | H | A | P | H | A | T | S |
| B | E | A | O | Z | R | N | N | T | B | B | H | E |
| U | S | Z | C | A | A | S | I | I | H | R | D | H |
| Z | S | A | D | O | C | E | J | D | S | A | A | A |
| Z | E | R | U | B | B | A | B | E | L | H | V | I |
| I | O | N | O | F | H | M | G | B | O | A | I | S |
| A | Z | O | R | E | H | O | B | O | A | M | D | O |
| H | A | I | R | U | D | N | O | M | L | A | S | J |

________________________________________

________________________________________

## FIND THE FALSE ONE

*One statement in each group of three below is not true, according to the book of Matthew. Can you find the false statements?*

1. a. John the Baptist wore a garment of camel's hair.
   b. John the Baptist ate manna.
   c. John the Baptist ate locusts.
2. a. Jesus turned stones to bread.
   b. Jesus fasted 40 days.
   c. Jesus taught in synagogues.
3. a. Only one apostle was named James.
   b. Only one apostle was named Andrew.
   c. Only one apostle was named Matthew.
4. a. The sower's seeds fell on stony ground.
   b. The sower's seeds fell among thorns.
   c. The sower's seeds fell in the river.
5. a. Five of the ten virgins were foolish.
   b. Five of the ten virgins were wise.
   c. Five of the ten virgins were beautiful.
6. a. Jesus told the parable of the mustard seed.
   b. Jesus told the parable of the five loaves of bread.
   c. Jesus told the parable of the wheat and tares.
7. a. Jesus was tempted to turn stones into bread.
   b. Jesus was tempted to turn water into wine.
   c. Jesus was tempted to throw himself from the temple pinnacle.
8. a. Jesus ate the Last Supper on the Sabbath.
   b. The disciples picked corn on the Sabbath.
   c. Jesus healed a withered hand on the Sabbath.
9. a. A leper was named Simon.
   b. A disciple was named Simon.
   c. The father of a lame boy was named Simon.
10. a. When Jesus was crucified, the earth quaked.
    b. When Jesus was crucified, hail rained from heaven.
    c. When Jesus was crucified, darkness covered the land.

## 37 SCRAMBLED BEATITUDES

*The Beatitudes are a wonderful blessing to all who read them. The first eight beatitudes from Matthew 5 are listed below, but the main words and phrases in parentheses have been scrambled. All of the letters are there, but in the wrong order. See if you can unscramble them to make sense of each beatitude.*

1. Blessed are the (PRISON PI TRIO): ______________________
   for theirs is the (DEAF HOG MONK VINE). ______________________
2. Blessed are they that (RUN MO): ______________________
   for they shall be (MET FOR COD). ______________________
3. Blessed are the (KEME): ______________________
   for they shall (REHEAT THEIR HINT). ______________________
4. Blessed are they which do (HUNT RANGED SHIRT) after righteousness: ______
   ______________________
   for they shall (FEED BILL). ______________________
5. Blessed are the (FURL MICE): ______________________
   for they shall (TRIM YE BACON). ______________________
6. Blessed are the (RAIN UP THERE): ______________________
   for they shall (GO SEED). ______________________
7. Blessed are the (PEEK CAMERAS): ______________________
   for they shall be called the (GOOF NERD CHILD). ______________________
8. Blessed are they which are persecuted for (SINGER STEAKHOUSES): ________
   ______________________
   for theirs is the (HONKED MANGO FIVE). ______________________

## 38 HIDDEN ANIMALS

*Many animals (four-footed, winged, finned, and buzzing) are named in the book of Matthew. See how many you can find lurking about in the sentences below. The letters in the names of the animals are found in unbroken, consecutive order, in at least two words. Disregard any punctuation marks when underlining the names.*

1. The wise men came later to Bethlehem; Matthew says Jesus was in a house at the time.
2. A real treat for the guests was loin of ox, especially when served with soy sauce.
3. Jesus said, "Bless them that curse you; do good to them that hate you."
4. With plenty of rest between games, the competitors win enough trophies to fill the case.
5. The disciples asked Jesus what would be a sign at the end of time, at His Second Coming.
6. In emergency situations, protocol takes a backseat to survivorship.
7. At creation, the Spirit of God hovered over the face of the waters.
8. When invited to a celebrity tea, Glenda gladly accepted.
9. "I'll just use the Wi-Fi," she said as she opened her new laptop.
10. If you want precise lettering, a laser pen takes the least amount of time.
11. After sampling the Polo, customers usually sniff of the Nautica next.
12. Seeing that he did well with the talents, his master gave him others to add to them.
13. In a strange turn of events, Alec saw a silver fox en route to Moscow.
14. Apparitions come in various forms—ghost, banshee, phantom, poltergeist—in fiction.
15. More oafish than chic, Ken sauntered into the room like a rhino in a rose garden.

## 39 SYLLABLE BY SYLLABLE

*Answer each definition below by putting together the syllables below, one letter for each blank. The number in parentheses indicates the number of syllables in that answer. When all of the answers are filled in properly, a quotation of Jesus can be found by reading the first and last letters of the answers top to bottom.*

A BAF BAY BLE BURGH E E ED EL EZ FIN GAT I
IN IN LAKE LEC LET LIKE LIP MIZ MOST NESS NOU
O O O ON OR PER POS RA RED RI SAU SEN SI SIS
SIS SUM TAR TE TIDE TRIC UP VA WITCH YULE ZOU

Resemblance (2) __ __ __ __ __ __ __ __

Desert refuge (3) __ __ __ __ __

Personal servant (2) __ __ __ __ __

Capital of Scotland (3) __ __ __ __ __ __ __ __ __

Christmastime (2) __ __ __ __ __ __ __ __

North American marsupial (3) __ __ __ __ __ __ __

_____ rooms at feasts..." (Matt. 23:6) (3) __ __ __ __ __ __ __ __ __

*Wake of the* ___ _____ (1949 John Wayne film, 2 words) (2) __ __ __ __ __ __ __ __

Coworker of Nehemiah (2) __ __ __ __

Confectionery with nuts or fruit (2) __ __ __ __ __ __

Type of guitar or toothbrush (3) __ __ __ __ __ __ __ __

Midwestern college nickname (2) __ __ __ __ __ __

Within bounds (4) __ __ __ __ __ __ __ __

Word omission (3) __ __ __ __ __ __ __ __

Levelheaded (3) __ __ __ __ __ __ __ __

Body of water between Canada and Greenland (2 words) (3) __ __ __ __ __ __ __ __ __

One of five "Greats" (2 words) (5) __ __ __ __ __ __ __ __ __ __ __

Jacob's twin (2) __ __ __ __

## THE DISCIPLES

*How much do you know about the disciples? All of the facts below are from the book of Matthew. Some names may be used more than once.*

1. Which disciple is the only one whose wife is mentioned in the Bible? ___________
2. Which disciple was Peter's brother? ___________
3. Which disciples were the sons of Zebedee? ___________
4. Which disciple committed suicide? ___________
5. Which disciple was a publican (tax collector)? ___________
6. Which disciple was the son of Alphaeus? ___________
7. Which disciples saw Jesus transfigured? ___________
8. Which disciple was the Canaanite? ___________
9. Which disciple walked on water? ___________
10. Which disciple betrayed Jesus? ___________
11. Which disciples' mother asked a special favor of Jesus? ___________
12. Which disciple denied knowing Jesus? ___________
13. Which disciples were given power to heal sickness and disease? ___________

    ___________
14. Which disciples asked Jesus whether He were the One "that should come," or should they wait for another? ___________

# THE GOSPEL ACCORDING TO ST. MARK

## SCAVENGER HUNT

*Can you find:*

1. Tiny arachnids in Mark 12:42 ______________________
2. A policeman's patrolled area in Mark 4:37______________________
3. A southpaw in Mark 14:13______________________
4. A timepiece in Mark 14:38______________________
5. A season in Mark 4:27 ______________________
6. A beaver's home in Mark 4:32 ______________________
7. A frozen treat in Mark 6:11 ______________________
8. A laundry detergent in Mark 6:50 ______________________
9. A credit card user in Mark 6:25 ______________________
10. A baseball team in Mark 8:38 ______________________
11. A pro football player in Mark 11:2______________________
12. Parts of a clock in Mark 7:2 ______________________

## 2 MOVIN' UP 1

*Move the letters in each column up and into the boxes above (not necessarily in the order the letters are in now) to find a quote from Jesus in the book of Mark. A block signifies the end of a word.*

| | | ■ | | ■ | | | | | | ■ | | | ■ | |
|---|---|---|---|---|---|---|---|---|---|---|---|---|---|---|
| | | | | | | ■ | | | | | | | | ■ |
| | | | | | | ■ | | | | | ■ | | | |
| | | ■ | | | | | | | ■ | | | | | |

| I | E | I | A | A | D | N | A | G | A | I | B | A | N | D |
|---|---|---|---|---|---|---|---|---|---|---|---|---|---|---|
| I | F | S | C | E | F | O | O | H | A | S | N | E | O | D |
| I | T | | D | L | H | | T | S | E | T | T | H | T | U |
| S | V | | E | | N | | U | T | | | | S | | |

## 3 ADD-A-LETTER 1

*Begin with the letter shown, then add one letter at each step, rearranging the letters each time to fit the definition at the left. The last answer will be a keyword from the book of Mark.*

Article
Moving vehicle
Wind direction indicator
Place of safety
God's abode

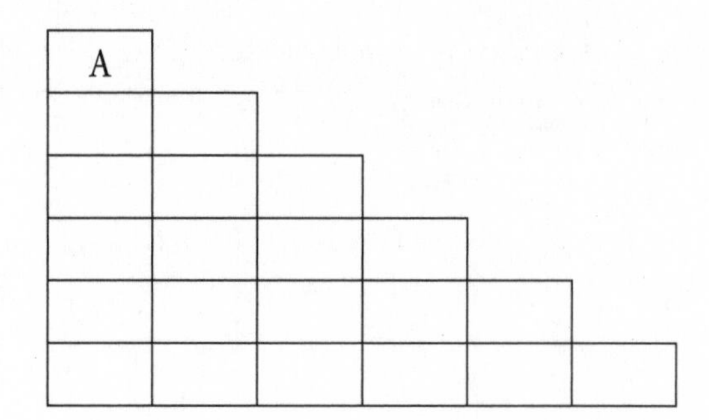


## 4 LEFTOVERS

*Answer the quiz questions below. The answers may be found in the list of words, though not necessarily in order. Cross off each answer from the list. The remaining words, when read left to right, top to bottom, will reveal a quotation from the book of Mark.*

| | | | |
|---|---|---|---|
| With | Wine | God | Work |
| Without | All | Three | Things |
| Love | Will | Four | Fingers |
| Are | Touch | Possible | Fishes |

1. Jesus said that new __________ must be put into new bottles (2:22).
2. Jesus said, "I will destroy this temple … and build another made __________ hands (14:58).
3. How many disciples saw Jesus transfigured? (9:2)
4. What, along with bread, did Jesus use to feed 5,000 men? (6:41)
5. In his own country, because of unbelief, Jesus could do no "mighty __________" (6:5).
6. Jesus said, "Thou shalt __________ thy neighbor as thyself" (12:31).
7. "If I may __________ but his clothes, I shall be whole" (5:28).
8. What did Jesus put in the deaf man's ears to heal him? (7:33)
9. How many men let down the palsied man through the roof? (2:3)
10. Jesus said that His brothers and sisters are those who do God's __________ (3:35).

______________________________________________

## 5 A-MAZE-ING QUOTE

*Find your way through this unique maze from start to finish by solving the clues below, whose answers comprise a quotation by Jesus from the book of Mark. The answer to each clue is a word in the quotation, given in order (clue 1 is the first word; clue 2 is the second, etc.). The number of letters in each answer has been given to help you. The quotation is hidden inside of the maze, with words in order, from start to finish. The string of words within the maze can move forward, backward, horizontally, vertically, or diagonally, and even change direction within a word, but never skips a letter, or crosses over itself.*

| ↓ | | | | | | | | | | | | | | |
|---|---|---|---|---|---|---|---|---|---|---|---|---|---|---|
| I | J | O | V | C | E | R | N | O | T | Y | M | N | E | E |
| T | K | B | Z | I | W | F | A | C | E | X | A | B | C | D |
| I | L | P | S | R | C | O | Q | U | B | F | D | O | A | L |
| S | E | A | Y | H | M | R | P | R | G | O | G | Y | F | E |
| X | R | M | R | A | D | A | C | A | M | E | X | I | T | R |
| T | N | O | O | W | I | V | L | D | E | Y | M | H | L | N |
| E | E | H | C | B | O | G | O | T | L | E | A | C | O | E |
| R | O | J | Y | T | N | E | W | R | E | R | N | Q | H | D |
| I | T | A | H | P | D | X | O | H | O | W | F | U | T | R |
| N | N | R | O | U | G | H | T | P | B | O | G | E | O | B |
| T | X | A | D | E | F | M | E | S | R | U | D | G | C | E |
| O | C | J | M | H | C | I | R | A | C | W | E | A | R | N |
| R | T | F | O | B | E | N | L | D | P | R | K | M | E | O |
| E | S | H | K | I | N | G | D | S | E | C | U | T | R | E |
| N | I | W | E | R | A | F | K | O | M | O | F | G | O | D |
| | | | | | | | | | | | | | | ↓ |

1. Impersonal pronoun (2) ________
2. Exists (2) ________
3. Less difficult (6) ________
4. Homonym of four (3) ________
5. Indefinite article (1) ________
6. Dromedary (5) ________
7. Toward (2) ________
8. Leave (2) ________
9. Done (7) ________
10. Indefinite article (3) ________
11. Hurricane center (3) ________
12. From (2) ________
13. Indefinite article (1) ________
14. Seamstress's tool (6) ________
15. "Lower ___ a snake..." (4) ________
16. "Tea ___ Two" (3) ________
17. Indefinite article (1) ________
18. Wealthy (4) ________
19. Human male (3) ________
20. Homonym of "two" (2) ________
21. Go in (5) ________
22. In (4) ________
23. Indefinite article (3) ________
24. Realm (7) ________
25. Small preposition (2) ________
26. Supreme deity (3) ________

## 6 A PROCESS OF ELIMINATION 1

*Follow the directions below, eliminating items from the word list. When the correct items have been removed, the remaining words, reading left to right, top to bottom, will reveal a quotation from the book of Mark.*

1. Delete all pro football mascots.
2. Delete all palindromes.
3. Delete all words that rhyme with *signed.*
4. Delete all anagrams for the word *dens.*
5. Delete all words in the first line of "The Star-Spangled Banner."
6. Delete all words containing three consecutive letters of the alphabet.
7. Delete all parts of speech known as articles.
8. Delete all names of US presidents.
9. Delete all words that combine with *ball* to make a compound word.
10. Delete all financial tools for transferring property.

| | | |
|---|---|---|
| Send | Grant | A |
| Find | Oh | Say |
| Will | Dined | Ewe |
| See | First | Have |
| Can | Pierce | The |
| Trust | Did | Eagles |
| Faith | Ends | Eye |
| Ravens | In | Deft |
| God | Mind | Noon |
| Foot | Basket | Bush |

________________________________________

________________________________________

## 7 WORD LADDER 1

*Each ladder has five columns. Every answer in column A will have six letters; every answer in column B will have five; answers in column C will have four. After answering the definition for A1, drop one letter and rearrange the remaining five letters to make the answer for B1. Place the dropped letter into the box to the left of column A. Drop another letter from the B1 answer and rearrange the remaining four letters to form the answer for C1. Place the dropped letter into the box to the right of column C. Continue this pattern for the entire puzzle. When finished, the columns of dropped letters, reading down, will reveal a compound word or phrase from the book of Mark.*

| | | A | | | | | | | B | | | | | C | | | |
|---|---|---|---|---|---|---|---|---|---|---|---|---|---|---|---|---|---|
| 1 | | | | | | | | | | | | | | | | | |
| 2 | | | | | | | | | | | | | | | | | |
| 3 | | | | | | | | | | | | | | | | | |
| 4 | | | | | | | | | | | | | | | | | |
| 5 | | | | | | | | | | | | | | | | | |

A1. Confuse
A2. Certain sauce
A3. _______ but goodies
A4. Shy
A5. Belittle

B1. Royal
B2. Fido's reward
B3. Rich veins
B4. Scholarly works
B5. Pointed out

C1. Actual
C2. Singer James
C3. Toboggan
C4. Bloom holder
C5. College head

## 8 MOVIN' UP 2

*Move the letters in each column up and into the boxes above (not necessarily in the order the letters are in now) to find a quote from Jesus in the book of Mark. A block signifies the end of a word.*

| | | | | | | | | | | | |
|---|---|---|---|---|---|---|---|---|---|---|---|
| | | | | ■ | | | | | | ■ | |
| ■ | | | | ■ | | | | | ■ | | |
| ■ | | | | | | | | | ■ | | |
| | ■ | | | | ■ | | | | | ■ | ■ |
| R | E | A | C | H | A | H | A | E | L | F | A |
| W | H | A | I | S | G | I | G | E | L | I | N |
| | M | H | N | | S | N | O | L | | | O |
| | | X | T | | | S | V | U | | | |

## 9 LOCATION, LOCATION, LOCATION

*Select the correct answer to make true statements about the book of Mark. When the letters of the correct answers are read top to bottom, the name of the city where Mark wrote his book (generally agreed to by Bible scholars) will be revealed.*

1. Mark is the ___________ of the four gospels.
   C. first    J. longest    R. shortest
2. Mark ___________ the genealogy of Jesus.
   O. doesn't mention    E. details    A. questions
3. Mark has ___________ chapters.
   M. 16    R. 20    P. 28
4. Mark begins with the ministry of ___________.
   A. Paul    U. Jesus    E. John the Baptist
5. Mark follows the book of ___________.
   I. Matthew    S. Luke    R. John
6. Mark ends with the ___________ of Jesus.
   A. resurrection    T. ascension    N. baptism
7. The first verse of Mark calls Jesus the ___________.
   S. light of the world    L. son of Mary    A. Son of God
8. The last verse of Mark says the work of the disciples was confirmed with ___________.
   E. lightning    L. signs    U. a voice from heaven
9. Mark ___________ one of the 12 apostles.
   S. arrested    M. was    Y. was not

_______________________________________________

## SIGNS OF THE END

*In Mark 13, Jesus named various events that would signal the end of time as we know it. See how many of these signs you can find hidden in the grid below.*

Abomination [of desolation]
Affliction
Betrayals
Christ coming
Darkened sun
Deceivers
Earthquakes
Falling stars
False Christs
False prophets
Famines
Hatred
Published Gospel
Rumors of war
Signs
Troubles
Wars
Wonders

| | | | | | | | | | | | | | | |
|---|---|---|---|---|---|---|---|---|---|---|---|---|---|---|
| G | N | I | M | O | C | T | S | I | R | H | C | D | R | P |
| R | O | A | N | W | H | R | T | I | E | N | A | I | U | Q |
| F | O | B | S | O | A | O | S | N | G | R | S | B | M | O |
| A | S | O | T | N | T | U | I | G | O | T | L | E | O | N |
| M | E | M | E | D | R | B | R | S | R | I | Q | T | M | U |
| I | K | I | H | E | E | L | H | O | S | U | U | R | O | S |
| N | A | N | P | R | D | E | C | H | I | S | R | A | W | D |
| E | U | A | O | S | B | S | E | A | G | O | S | Y | O | E |
| S | Q | T | R | U | E | D | S | T | N | F | F | A | M | N |
| S | H | I | P | E | G | N | L | R | S | F | A | L | C | E |
| G | T | O | E | O | R | O | A | N | T | A | L | S | E | K |
| N | R | N | S | R | A | W | F | O | S | R | O | M | U | R |
| I | A | P | L | F | N | O | I | T | C | I | L | F | F | A |
| L | E | N | A | F | E | S | R | E | V | I | E | C | E | D |
| L | O | S | F | A | L | L | I | N | G | S | T | A | R | S |

## 11 CHAIN LINKS

*Place the five-letter answer of each clue into the boxes at the right. The answers form a chain: The last letter of each answer is the first letter of the next answer, and the last letter of the last answer is the first letter of the first answer. When all correct answers have been placed, the shaded column, reading top to bottom, will reveal a quotation of Jesus from the book of Mark.*

1. San Francisco's _______ cars
2. Vote into office
3. Eagle's claw
4. Nervous folks bite them
5. Strainer
6. Edges of roofs
7. Precipitous
8. Jordan's city of rock
9. "________ to ashes"
10. Vaporization
11. Gog and ________
12. Bride's partner
13. Folk or classical
14. Superhero's accessories
15. Take illegally
16. Fragrant shrub

| | | | | |
|---|---|---|---|---|
| | | | | |
| | | | | |
| | | | | |
| | | | | |
| | | | | |
| | | | | |
| | | | | |
| | | | | |
| | | | | |
| | | | | |
| | | | | |
| | | | | |
| | | | | |
| | | | | |
| | | | | |
| | | | | |

## 12 SYLLABLE BY SYLLABLE

*Answer each definition below by putting together the syllables from the box at the top, one letter for each blank. The number in parentheses indicates the number of syllables in that answer. When all of the answers are filled in properly, a quotation of Jesus can be found by reading the first and last letters of each answer top to bottom.*

A A A A A AC AH AH AL AM AN ATE BI BO
BRY CA CEL DER DOR DRI E E E EM ER ER EX
FAST GINT HER HEZ I I IN IVE JAH KI KON
KOV LI LIB LYD MER MORE NE NEV NIC O OL
PIS RAB SA SEP STEAD TANCE TION TLE TOW
TRAP TU TU UN VA VOL Y YU ZI

| | | |
|---|---|---|
| Judean king who got 15 extra years of life | (4) | ___ ___ ___ ___ ___ ___ ___ ___ |
| Home of Egypt's ancient lighthouse | (5) | ___ ___ ___ ___ ___ ___ ___ ___ ___ ___ |
| Famous Soviet cosmonaut of Soyuz 11 | (2) | ___ ___ ___ ___ ___ ___ |
| Romans or Hebrews | (3) | ___ ___ ___ ___ ___ ___ ___ ___ |
| Ancient provincial Persian governor | (2) | ___ ___ ___ ___ ___ ___ |
| Hasten | (4) | ___ ___ ___ ___ ___ ___ ___ ___ ___ ___ |
| Paul's first European convert | (3) | ___ ___ ___ ___ ___ |
| Ancient Roman garment | (2) | ___ ___ ___ ___ ___ |
| Possession passed from generation to generation | (4) | ___ ___ ___ ___ ___ ___ ___ ___ ___ ___ ___ |
| Moses viewed Promised Land from this mount | (2) | ___ ___ ___ ___ |
| Northern North American region | (2) | ___ ___ ___ ___ ___ |
| Mediterranean tree found in Gethsemane | (2) | ___ ___ ___ ___ ___ |
| Current beneath the surface | (3) | ___ ___ ___ ___ ___ ___ ___ ___ |
| Leader of Jewish synagogue | (2) | ___ ___ ___ ___ ___ |
| Unchanging | (2) | ___ ___ ___ ___ ___ ___ ___ ___ ___ |

Prophet during King Ahab's reign (3) ___ ___ ___ ___ ___ ___

Country in northern Africa (3) ___ ___ ___ ___ ___

Trip to Disneyland, maybe? (3) ___ ___ ___ ___ ___ ___ ___ ___

Organism in early stages of development (3) ___ ___ ___ ___ ___ ___

Greek version of Old Testament (4) ___ ___ ___ ___ ___ ___ ___ ___ ___ ___

Eighth king of Judah (4) ___ ___ ___ ___ ___ ___ ___

Raven's quote (3) ___ ___ ___ ___ ___ ___ ___ ___ ___

Gabled window (2) ___ ___ ___ ___ ___ ___

______________________________________________

______________________________________________

## 13 ADD-A-LETTER 2

*Begin with the letter shown, then add one letter at each step, rearranging the letters each time to fit the definition at the left. The last answer will be a key word from the book of Mark.*

Conjunction

Fish eggs

1948 Hitchcock film

Pre-surgery room (hyph.)

Frog or rabbit

Daniel or Elisha

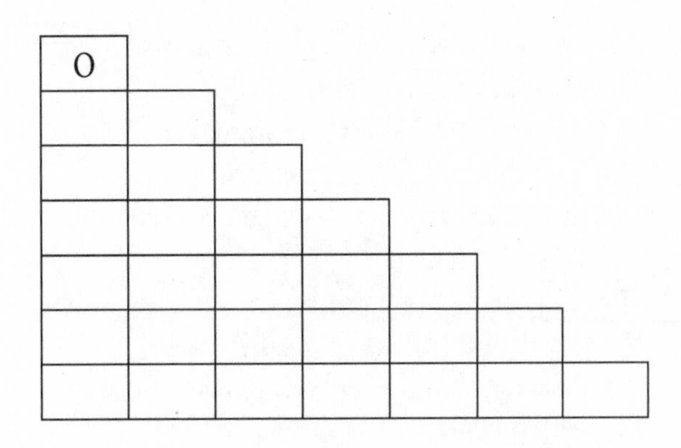

# 14 "MARK" MY WORDS

*Place each clue's answer in the corresponding boxes, one letter to each box. Every answer will contain the word "Mark" as indicated. When all of the answers have been filled in correctly, the shaded column, reading down, will reveal a nickname for the disciples, given by Jesus in the book of Mark.*

| | | | | | | | | | | | | | | | | | |
|---|---|---|---|---|---|---|---|---|---|---|---|---|---|---|---|---|---|
| 1. | | | M | A | R | K | | | | | | | | | | | |
| 2. | M | A | R | K | | | | | | | | | | | | | |
| 3. | | | | | | | | | | | | | M | A | R | K | |
| 4. | | | | | | | | | | | | M | A | R | K | | |
| 5. | | | | | | | | | M | A | R | K | | | | | |
| 6. | | | | | | | | | | M | A | R | K | | | | |
| 7. | | | | | | | | | | M | A | R | K | | | | |
| 8. | M | A | R | K | | | | | | | | | | | | | |
| 9. | | | | | | | | | | | | M | A | R | K | | |
| 10 | | | M | A | R | K | | | | | | | | | | | |
| 11. | | | | | | | | | M | A | R | K | | | | | |
| 12. | | | | | | | | | M | A | R | K | | | | | |

1. Without this, no one could buy or sell in Revelation 13 (4 words)
2. Tom Sawyer's creator (2 words)
3. Interrogative indicator (2 words)
4. Indicator of quality or excellence
5. Registered product identifier
6. Casual comment
7. Date on a piece of mail
8. Lover of Cleopatra (2 words)
9. Where to buy secondhand items (2 words)
10. Sharpshooter
11. Seller of goods by phone
12. Southernmost Nordic country

______________________________________________

______________________________________________

## 15 WORD LADDER 2

*Each ladder has five columns. Every answer in column A will have five letters; every answer in column B will have four; answers in column C will have three. After answering the definition for A1, drop one letter and rearrange the remaining four letters to make the answer for B1. Place the dropped letter into the box to the left of column A. Drop another letter from the B1 answer and rearrange the remaining three letters to form the answer for C1. Place the dropped letter into the box to the right of column C. Continue this pattern for the entire puzzle. When finished, the columns of dropped letters, reading down, will reveal a phrase from the book of Mark.*

| | | A | | | | | B | | | | C | | | |
|---|---|---|---|---|---|---|---|---|---|---|---|---|---|---|
| 1 | | | | | | | | | | | | | | |
| 2 | | | | | | | | | | | | | | |
| 3 | | | | | | | | | | | | | | |
| 4 | | | | | | | | | | | | | | |
| 5 | | | | | | | | | | | | | | |
| 6 | | | | | | | | | | | | | | |
| 7. | | | | | | | | | | | | | | |

A1. Float freely
A2. Cruel
A3. Travel plan
A4. Colander, e.g.
A5. Characteristic
A6. Male bee
A7. Portrait casing

B1. Soil
B2. Former Persian title
B3. Ripped
B4. Nights before
B5. Actress Hayworth
B6. Tear
B7. Old gray ______

C1. Free from
C2. Residue
C3. Scrap
C4. View
C5. _______ and feather
C6. Crimson
C7. Dodge truck model

## CHANGE-A-LETTER

*Change one letter in every word below to make another word. When the correct letters have been replaced, a quotation of Jesus from the book of Mark will be revealed.*

IT AND MAY DETIRE GO BY FIEST, THY DAME STALL ME LIST IF ILL ANY SHE SERPANT OR AIL.

______________________________________________

______________________________________________

## 17 MISSING LINKS

*Fill in the five blanks of each answer with the rearranged letters of one of the five-letter words from the column at right. Each clue's answer will be a 10-letter word from the book of Mark.*

| | Clue | | | | | | | | | | | |
|---|---|---|---|---|---|---|---|---|---|---|---|---|
| 1. | Remote area | | | L | | E | | N | | S | S | pines |
| 2. | Evil | | | C | K | | D | | E | S | | heart |
| 3. | Age group | | | N | | | A | T | I | O | | cliff |
| 4. | Sympathy | | O | | | | S | | I | O | N | slant |
| 5. | Comprehend | U | N | | | | S | | | N | D | riled |
| 6. | Ownership | | O | S | | | S | S | | O | | trade |
| 7. | Tactfully | | | S | C | | E | | T | | Y | camps |
| 8. | Greeting | | A | | U | T | | | I | O | | wider |
| 9. | Ground shaking | E | A | | | | Q | U | | K | | swine |
| 10. | Hardship | A | | | | I | | T | | O | N | green |

## 18 THE WORD WITHIN

*Fill in the blanks with words which, when combined with the letters present, will answer each clue. The words will be of varying lengths. When read top to bottom, the words that fill the blanks will reveal a quotation from the book of Mark.*

| | Clue | |
|---|---|---|
| 1. | National ________ | AN ________ M |
| 2. | Shakespeare work | ________ NET |
| 3. | Easy | S ________ T |
| 4. | Certain Italians | RO ________ S |
| 5. | Having two legislative chambers | BI ________ RAL |
| 6. | Tale | S ________ RY |
| 7. | Bestowed, as a gift | ________ N |
| 8. | Woodworking tool | C ________ EL |
| 9. | 1944 Hitchcock film | ________ BOAT |
| 10. | Bad actor | H ________ M |
| 11. | Hinged window above a door | T ________ |
| 12. | Prom dress | ________ MAL |
| 13. | Home to Bavaria | GER ________ |

## THE TWELVE DISCIPLES

*Fill in the names of the twelve disciples from Mark 3:16–19. The names have been listed below.*

T
H
E
D
I
S
C
I
P
L
E
S

| | | |
|---|---|---|
| Simon Peter | James | John |
| Andrew | Philip | Bartholomew |
| Matthew | Thomas | James |
| Thaddaeus | Simon | Judas Iscariot |

20

## ADD-A-LETTER 3

*Begin with the letter shown, then add one letter at each step, rearranging the letters each time to fit the definition at the left. The last answer of each puzzle will be a key word from the book of Mark.*

A

Pa's better half

Limb

Female horse

Lion trainer

What the disciples called Jesus in Mark 4:38

## 21 CLASSIFIEDS

*Of course, newspapers did not exist at the time Mark wrote his book, but if they did, the following classified ads might have been placed. Can you match the ad to the person or persons who might have placed it?*

a. Levi (Matthew)
b. Joseph of Arimathaea
c. Daughter of Herodias
d. Bartimaeus
e. Jairus
f. Pharisees
g. James and John
h. Simon, the Cyrenian
i. Gadarene man
j. John the Baptist

1. FOR SALE: Tin cup and walking stick, used by former blind man. Inquire near Jericho. ___
2. Come one; come all! Revival at the River Jordan! Fervent preaching and baptisms daily. ___
3. DANCER FOR HIRE. Experienced. Recently performed at the palace. ___
4. REWARD – for information leading to the arrest and conviction of Jesus of Nazareth, wanted for blasphemy and healing on the Sabbath. ___
5. TOMB FOR SALE. Used only once, and only for three days. Inquire in Jerusalem with Sanhedrin. ___
6. FOR SALE: Fishing nets. Inquire at the house of Zebedee in Bethsaida. ___
7. YOU'RE INVITED! My daughter is celebrating her 13th birthday, which we never thought she would see. Join in the celebration, first day of next week. ___
8. INTRODUCTORY SPECIAL – This week only. Receive 20% discount off one year membership at Cyrene Gym. See Rufus or Alexander, my sons, for information. ___
9. FOR SALE: Money bag, previously used for collecting taxes. ___
10. WANTED: Room and board for man who most recently lived among the tombs and just evicted a legion of residents. ___

## 22 MISSING PERSONS

*See if you can find the names of 10 persons named in the book of Mark hidden in the sentences below. The letters of the names will be in consecutive order, reading left to right, and will be found in at least two words (for example: "Cheer up and be gl**ad**, **Am**ber!" might hide "Adam" as indicated in bold). Disregard punctuation and capitalization when locating each name. If you need them, the names of the missing persons are given alphabetically below.*

| Herod | Jairus | James | Joseph | Levi |
|---|---|---|---|---|
| Mary | Peter | Pilate | Salome | Thomas |

1. Like a crazed ninja, I rushed toward the judo expert with sword in hand.
2. In the Eaton Steeple Chase, the horse he rode was a well-trained steed.
3. While snorkeling, we saw two octopi; later, we spotted an eel.
4. Besides Oklahoma, rye is grown in Kansas, Nebraska, and Canada.
5. Eric loves peanut butter and jam, especially strawberry on raisin bread.
6. In the haunted Wellsford estate of San Jose, phantoms are said to roam the halls at night.
7. My Stradivarius is a valuable violin, crafted centuries ago.
8. One thing you should know about Sal—omelets are her favorite breakfast food.
9. Is a fathom as deep as a league?
10. Martha, for your sake, we certainly hope Terrance comes home soon.

## 23 KNOCKOUTS

*Below is a quotation of Jesus from the book of Mark. All of the words are there, in the correct order, with the letters in correct order as well, but one letter has been added to each word. "Knock out" the unnecessary letter in each word to reveal the quotation.*

MAY HOURSE SHALOL BME CEALLED ONF AILL
NAOTIONS THEM HOBUSE NOF PRLAYER, BOUT YOUR
SHAVE MALDE INT AS DEAN ORF THIERVES.

______________________________________________

______________________________________________

## WHO SAID THAT?

*Match the quotation with its attributed author, according to the book of Mark.*

a. Legion
b. John the Baptist
c. Pilate
d. A voice from the cloud
e. Jairus, ruler of the synagogue
f. Scribes
g. Peter
h. The Syrophenician woman
i. Father of the boy with the "dumb spirit"
j. The centurion at the cross
k. The daughter of Herodias
l. John
m. King Herod
n. Jesus
o. James and John

1. "Truly this man was the Son of God" (15:39). ___
2. "I indeed have baptized you with water: but he shall baptize you with the Holy Ghost" (1:8). ___
3. "For whosoever shall do the will of God, the same is my brother, and my sister, and mother" (3:35). ___
4. "It is John, whom I beheaded: he is risen from the dead" (6:16). ___
5. "My little daughter lieth at the point of death" (5:23). ___
6. "Yes, Lord: yet the dogs under the table eat of the children's crumbs" (7:28). ___
7. "This is my beloved Son: hear him" (9:7). ___
8. "Master, we saw one casting out devils in thy name, and he followeth not us: and we forbad him" (9:38). ___
9. "Art thou the King of the Jews?" (15:2). ___
10. "Who can forgive sins but God only?" (2:7). ___
11. "I will that thou give me by and by in a charger the head of John the Baptist" (6:25). ___
12. "Lord, I believe; help thou mine unbelief" (9:24). ___
13. "What have I to do with thee, Jesus, thou Son of the most high God?" (5:7). ___
14. "Thou art the Christ" (8:29). ___
15. "Grant unto us that we may sit, one on thy right hand, and the other on thy left hand, in thy glory" (10:37). ___

## 25 CROSSROADS

*Each crossroad below contains two words that make a phrase from the book of Mark. Fill in the blanks from the word list below. The first word of each phrase should be placed down, and the second word across.*

| | | | |
|---|---|---|---|
| Again | Day | Mites | Rise |
| Burnt | Days | Money | Temple |
| Changer | Feast | Offering | Two |
| Chief | Forty | Priest | Veil |

1.

2.

3.

4.

5.

6.

7.

8.

## 26 MOVIN' UP 3

*Move the letters in each column up and into the boxes above (not necessarily in the order the letters are in now) to find a quote from Jesus in the book of Mark. A block signifies the end of a word.*

|   |   |   |   |   |   |   |   |   | ■ |   |   |   |   |
|---|---|---|---|---|---|---|---|---|---|---|---|---|---|
|   | ■ |   |   |   |   |   |   |   | ■ |   |   |   | ■ |
|   |   | ■ |   |   |   |   | ■ |   |   |   |   |   |   |
|   |   | ■ |   |   | ■ |   |   | ■ |   |   |   |   | ■ |
|   |   |   |   |   |   |   |   |   | ■ |   |   | ■ | ■ |
| E | E | C | E | C | C | E | E | C | H | A | E | A | L |
| L | F | O | E | I | E | H | T | E | N | I | H | D | R |
| O | H | R | I | N | E | I | V | H |   | M | L | E |   |
| R | N |   | S | O | V | M | Y | R |   | O | M | E |   |
| W |   |   | S | U |   | V |   |   |   | S | N |   |   |

## 27 MIXED BLESSINGS

*Find each two-word phrase below by sorting the letters for each word. The letters of each word are given in the correct order, but the two words have been mixed. For example, "blue moon" could be "B L M U O E O N." Each phrase is from the book of Mark. A hint, if you need it, has been given for each one.*

1. BTASKWEELVETS ______________________ (woven products)
2. HANGOLELSY ______________________ (messengers)
3. COGMFOODORT ______________________ (coziness)
4. RUPPOERMOOMSTS ______________________ (attics)
5. POWIDOROW ______________________ (Naomi)
6. SSWPEEICTES ______________________ (cinnamon)
7. HIPRIEGSHT ______________________ (head man)
8. WGHAIRTMENET ______________________ (bleach)
9. BLIMANND ______________________ (Braille)
10. BESLOOVEND ______________________ (offspring)

# 28 ACROSTIC

*Answer each clue, and then transfer the letters from the blanks to the grid according to the number under each blank. A quotation from the book of Mark will be revealed in the grid. As letters are filled into the grid, words will become apparent. Fill in the letters to these words and transfer those letters to the clues below, according to the letter and the number in each square. A solid block indicates the end of a word. Also, when the first letters of each clue's answer are read top to bottom, the name of the person who spoke the quotation will be revealed.*

| G 1 | A 2 | B 3 | | J 4 | K 5 | G 6 | D 7 | E 8 | | D 9 | I 10 |
|---|---|---|---|---|---|---|---|---|---|---|---|
| I 11 | C 12 | J 13 | | A 14 | K 15 | C 16 | | B 17 | D 18 | K 19 | G 20 |
| F 21 | F 22 | J 23 | C 24 | | A 25 | E 26 | A 27 | K 28 | F 29 | E 30 | G 31 |
| D 32 | | H 33 | E 34 | | B 35 | B 36 | I 37 | C 38 | H 39 | F 40 | |
| J 41 | E 42 | A 43 | | G 44 | H 45 | F 46 | B 47 | | J 48 | K 49 | |
| F 50 | F 51 | D 52 | | C 53 | A 54 | H 55 | I 56 | E 57 | C 58 | | |

A. Father-in-law of Moses ___ ___ ___ ___ ___ ___
27 43 14 2 25 54

B. Receded ___ ___ ___ ___ ___
36 17 35 3 47

C. Pele's sport ___ ___ ___ ___ ___ ___
24 38 53 12 16 58

D. Single ___ ___ ___ ___ ___
18 7 9 52 32

E. Boil ___ ___ ___ ___ ___ ___
34 57 8 30 42 26

F. Broke the rules ___ ___ ___ ___ ___ ___ ___
29 51 22 46 50 40 21

G. *Grand* ________ (1932 movie) ___ ___ ___ ___ ___
44 6 1 31 20

H. Frost ___ ___ ___ ___
55 33 39 45

I. Twelfth of a foot ___ ___ ___ ___
11 56 37 10

J. Zacchaeus's distinguishing trait ___ ___ ___ ___ ___
4 13 48 23 41

K. Robber ___ ___ ___ ___ ___
5 15 19 28 49

## 29 WRITER'S BLOCKS

*Mark identifies many places as he tells the story of Christ. In each row of blocks below is the name of a location, but the name has been divided into blocks of three letters or less and mixed up. The letters within each block are in order, but the blocks are not. Oh, and an extra block of letters has been added for fun. Take away the unneeded block and put the others in order to find 10 locations.*

| | | | | | |
|---|---|---|---|---|---|
| JER | USA | HO | IC | | ______ |
| ZA | NA | RE | TH | ST | ______ |
| LEE | CA | GA | LI | | ______ |
| NAU | TO | M | ER | CAP | ______ |
| HSA | BET | RAC | IDA | | ______ |
| MET | APO | LIS | DEC | | ______ |
| GET | HER | MAN | E | HSE | ______ |
| BE | AN | TH | IS | Y | ______ |
| GOT | JOR | HA | GOL | | ______ |
| A | JUD | E | COR | | ______ |

## 30 ONE AT A TIME

*Fill in the missing letters to make common four-letter words below. Then transfer those letters to the corresponding numbers in the grid. The three-word phrase that will be revealed in the grid is the answer to the question. Be careful; more than one letter will make a complete word, but only one letter will correctly complete the phrase in the grid.*

1. s__op
2. cas__
3. l__an
4. sp__n
5. nea__
6. __ood
7. f__re
8. min__
9. __rip
10. sa__e
11. lon__
12. we__t
13. l__mp
14. __ore
15. dar__

Question: What do John the Baptist and Winnie the Pooh have in common?

__ __ __ __ __    __ __ __ __ __ __    __ __ __ __

1 2 3 4 5    6 7 8 9 10 11    12 13 14 15

## 31 MARK'S MALADIES

*Mark records that Jesus healed many people of disease and afflictions. The list below consists of many names of these maladies (and a few more from other places in the Bible) in code. When you have identified a word in the list, use the solved letters to help decode other words in the same list. For example, KDBBDF could be LETTER. A starting hint is given at the bottom of the page if you need it.*

U O X T Y Z W

_ _ _ _ _ _ _

K O B L G O Z Z

_ _ _ _ _ _ _ _

N U V G K G O Z Z

_ _ _ _ _ _ _ _ _

V Z Z R O Y L N U Y Y K

_ _ _ _ _ _ _ _ _ _ _ _

Z C B U U X Y A

_ _ _ _ _ _ _ _

X B T B U W Z V Z

_ _ _ _ _ _ _ _ _

L O S O T

_ _ _ _ _

C R D O G O Z Z

_ _ _ _ _ _ _ _

E V D J O T O K J B G K

_ _ _ _ _ _ _ _ _ _ _ _

U B C O G O Z Z

_ _ _ _ _ _ _ _

K O C Y G X Y Z Z O Z Z V Y G

_ _ _ _ _ _ _ _ _ _ _ _ _ _ _

X U B P R O

_ _ _ _ _ _

Starting hint: G = N

## 32 WORD LADDER 3

*Each ladder has five columns. Every answer in column A will have five letters; every answer in column B will have four; answers in column C will have three. After answering the definition for A1, drop one letter and rearrange the remaining four letters to make the answer for B1. Place the dropped letter into the box to the left of column A. Drop another letter from the B1 answer and rearrange the remaining three letters to form the answer for C1. Place the dropped letter into the box to the right of column C. Continue this pattern for the entire puzzle. When finished, the columns of dropped letters, reading down, will reveal a phrase from the book of Mark.*

| | | A | | | | | B | | | | C | | | |
|---|---|---|---|---|---|---|---|---|---|---|---|---|---|---|
| 1 | | | | | | | | | | | | | | |
| 2 | | | | | | | | | | | | | | |
| 3 | | | | | | | | | | | | | | |
| 4 | | | | | | | | | | | | | | |
| 5 | | | | | | | | | | | | | | |
| 6 | | | | | | | | | | | | | | |
| 7 | | | | | | | | | | | | | | |
| 8 | | | | | | | | | | | | | | |
| 9 | | | | | | | | | | | | | | |
| 10 | | | | | | | | | | | | | | |
| 11 | | | | | | | | | | | | | | |

A1. Clothed
A2. Cord
A3. 45 rpm material
A4. A synthetic fabric
A5. Suspend a motion
A6. Bald ______
A7. Camera accessory
A8. More mature
A9. Speak at length
A10. Motion picture
A11. Recorded

B1. Bicycled
B2. Esau, to Jacob
B3. Roman historian
B4. Not one
B5. Cain's brother
B6. Joy
B7. Whip
B8. Dock
B9. Memorization by repetition
B10. Transport
B11. Top of the head

C1. Rosy
C2. Humor
C3. ______ League
C4. Fled
C5. Meadow
C6. Hair product
C7. Owns
C8. Each
C9. Decay
C10. A Stooge
C11. Spigot

## 33 FILL IN THE BLANK

*Fill in the blanks below with the correct word to complete each sentence. When all words have been filled in correctly, the answers, when read top to bottom, will reveal a quotation of Jesus from the book of Mark.*

1. "And he began to teach them, that the Son of man must ___________________ many things."
2. "They uncovered ___________________ roof where he was."
3. "My ___________________ daughter lies at the point of death."
4. "Whoever shall receive one of such ___________________ in my name receives me."
5. "Render ___________________ Caesar the things that are Caesar's."
6. "___________________ out of the man, thou unclean spirit."
7. "… and the angels ministered ___________________ him."
8. "Follow ___________________."
9. "She broke the box ___________________ poured it on his head."
10. "___________________ him not: for there is no man which shall do a miracle in my name, that can lightly speak evil of me."
11. "He taught ___________________ as one that had authority."
12. "… the latchet of whose shoes I am ___________________ worthy to stoop down and unloose."

_______________________________________________________________

_______________________________________________________________

## ONE OR THE OTHER

*Cross out one letter in each box so that the remaining letters will spell out a quotation from the book of Mark. A black box signifies the end of a word.*

| W M | H A | N E | N Y | ■ | S T | H P |
|---|---|---|---|---|---|---|
| A O | N T | ■ | A C | R A | N E | ■ |
| T F | I O | N R | S E | S T | ■ | S T |
| T H | A I | L N | E L | ■ | M B | E Y |
| ■ | F L | A I | S N | T E | ■ | B A |
| N A | D T | ■ | H T | I H | S E | ■ |
| R L | E A | M S | T P | ■ | S F | T I |
| R A | S N | D T | ■ | ■ | ■ | ■ |

______________________________________________

______________________________________________

## 35 MISSING VOWELS

*A seven-word quotation from the book of Mark is below, but the vowels and spaces are missing. The missing vowels are listed above the quotation. Fill in the vowels and spaces to make a correct and complete quotation.*

Vowels: A A E E E O O O U

Quotation: T K P T H C R S S N D F L L W M

______________________________________________

______________________________________________

## PEOPLE AND PLACES

*The answers to the clues are in alphabetical order below. When all of the answers are filled in, the first letters, reading down, will reveal a quotation of Jesus from the book of Mark.*

| | | | | |
|---|---|---|---|---|
| Alphaeus | Elijah | Herod | Isaac | Tarsus |
| Amram | Elisha | Herodias | Lazarus | Thomas |
| Ananias | Elizabeth | Hophni | Mary | Timothy |
| Dorcas | Felix | Horeb | Onesimus | Wilderness |
| Eden | Hagar | Hur | Tabitha | Yeshua |

1. ______________ Doubting disciple
2. ______________ King Herod's sister-in-law
3. ______________ Hebrew spelling of Moses' successor
4. ______________ Paul appeared before this governor
5. ______________ Husband of Sapphira
6. ______________ Terah's grandson by Sarah
7. ______________ Peter raised her from the dead
8. ______________ Mother of Ishmael
9. ______________ Pilate sent Jesus to this person
10. ______________ Father of Moses
11. ______________ Paul's hometown
12. ______________ Mount where Moses brought water from the rock
13. ______________ Mother of Jesus
14. ______________ Father of Matthew
15. ______________ Peter raised her from the dead
16. ______________ Home of Adam and Eve
17. ______________ Eunice's son
18. ______________ He helped Aaron hold up Moses' hands
19. ______________ Prophet during reign of Ahab
20. ______________ Prophet who succeeded Elijah
21. ______________ Jesus was tempted here for forty days
22. ______________ Evil son of Eli
23. ______________ A slave of Philemon
24. ______________ Brother of Mary and Martha
25. ______________ Mother of John the Baptist

______________________________________________

## 37 QUOTATION CODE

*Each numbered puzzle below is a quotation of Jesus in code. Each puzzle has its own code: one letter stands for another letter, always the same one within each puzzle. When you have identified a word in the quotation, use the solved letters to help decode other words in the same quotation. For example, KDBBDF could be LETTER.*

1.

Q N M W Q E H U I C Q Z U Q L Q U X U

___ __ _____________ ____ _____________

M H M Q E Z F Q F Z X B N, F J M F

_____________ ___________ _______

W Q E H U I C T M E E I F Z F M E U.

_____________ ___________ _________

2.

W E K C E X P A N V B C A L N A X C R A

__ _____________ ____ _____ _____________

X C B C K, J R A N B X N V C L B

_________ _____ ____ _____ _____

M C R B A K O, W B F W S C B U X N V C L B

_____________ _____ _________ _____ _____

H N B W B F N B X N V C L B X C R V P.

_____ _____ ____ _____ _____ _________

3.

R U S D A D C  R X H H  Y S J D  V P I D C  J D,

_______ ____ ____ _____ __

H D I  U X J  N D Q F  U X J E D H P,  V Q N

___ ___ ____ ______ ___

I V O D  K W  U X E  Y C S E E,  V Q N

____ __ ___ _____ ___

P S H H S R  J D.

______ __

4.

Z P E M A M S  Z T D D  V B A M  P T V  D T Q M

_______ ____ ____ ___ ____

V P B D D  D E V M  T C;  G K C  Z P E M A M S

_____ ____ __ ___ _______

V P B D D  D E V M  P T V  D T Q M  Q E S  X L

_____ ____ ___ ____ ___ __

V B U M  B O R  C P M  Y E V H M D' V,  C P M

____ ___ ___ _______ ___

V B X M  V P B D D  V B A M  T C.

____ _____ ____ __

5.

S C  L H A  F N X  Z P O S P R P,  N O O

__ ___ ___ _______ ___

W T S X I Q  N J P  V H Q Q S Z O P  W H

______ ___ ________ __

T S B  W T N W  Z P O S P R P Q.

___ ____ ________

## 38 PROCESS OF ELIMINATION 2

*Follow the directions below, eliminating items from the word list. When the correct items have been removed, the remaining words, reading left to right, top to bottom, will reveal a quotation from the book of Mark.*

1. Delete all models of vehicles.
2. Delete all synonyms for help.
3. Delete all Christian names of Beatles.
4. Delete all words that form new words when read backward.
5. Delete all bodies of water.
6. Delete all prepositions.
7. Delete all words that form new words when the letter "m" is added to the end.
8. Delete all cards in a standard deck of cards.
9. Delete all words associated with the calendar.
10. Delete all personal pronouns.

| | | | | | |
|---|---|---|---|---|---|
| I | Keep | The | Seven | Paul | Days |
| See | His | Reward | John | By | Aid |
| Brook | Escape | Peace | Be | From | Was |
| Pilot | A | River | At | Comfort | Week |
| Liberty | Them | Accord | King | Of | Still |

______________________________

______________________________

## ADD-A-LETTER 4

*Begin with the letter shown, then add one letter at each step, rearranging the letters each time to fit the definition at the left. The last answer will be a key word from the book of Mark.*

| Clue | Answer |
|---|---|
| | O |
| Accomplish | _ _ |
| Female deer | _ _ _ |
| Bird of peace | _ _ _ _ |
| Managed a vehicle | _ _ _ _ _ |
| One who invalidates (something) | _ _ _ _ _ _ |
| A major topic of Mark 10; a marital split | _ _ _ _ _ _ _ |

# THE GOSPEL ACCORDING TO
# ST. LUKE

## 1 AWAY IN A MANGER

*The list below is a group of related words in code, where one letter stands for another. Within the same list, the code will stay the same. For example, KDBBDF could be LETTER. When you have identified a word in the list, use the solved letters to help decode other words in the same list. All of the entries in the list are from the book of Luke.*

X R M L D R L R B

__________________

Z A N R D K

____________

K S Z T T D J A N V D C M L R K

__________________ ______________

A C I C C B J A M L R J A A

___ _______ ___ _____ _____

H C K R E L

____________

K L R E L R I T K

__________________

A J N L M

__________

X Z X W

________

B Z I W

________

E R Z V R C A R Z I M L

__________ ___ __________

## 2 ADD-A-LETTER 1

*Begin with the letter shown, then add one letter at each step, rearranging the letters each time to fit the definition at the left. The last answer will be a key word from the book of Luke.*

| Clue | Answer |
|---|---|
| | A |
| Sixth note of singing scale | _ _ |
| Meadow | _ _ _ |
| Valley | _ _ _ _ |
| Seedless orange | _ _ _ _ _ |
| "Beware of the _______ of the Pharisees." | _ _ _ _ _ _ |

## 3 MOVIN' UP 1

*Move the letters in each column up and into the boxes above (not necessarily in the order the letters are in now) to find a quote from Jesus in the book of Luke. A block signifies the end of a word.*

| | | | | | | | | | | |
|---|---|---|---|---|---|---|---|---|---|---|
| | | | | | | | ■ | | | ■ |
| | | | ■ | | | | | ■ | | |
| | ■ | | | ■ | | | | | | |
| B | H | E | F | L | E | D | D | A | E | L |
| D | L | E | S | S | I | R | R | B | E | O |
| T | | O | | | O | S | | | G | |

## 4 TAKE-A-LETTER

*Each word in the verse from Luke below has an extra letter. The letters are in the correct order; the words are in the correct order. Take away the unnecessary letters (and punctuation where necessary) to make the verse correct.*

"SEVEN THEN EVERY CHAIRS OFT YOU'RE HEARD CARE FALL NUMBEDRED"

______________________________

______________________________

## 5 ACROSTIC

*Answer each clue, then transfer the letters from the blanks to the grid according to the number under each blank. A quotation from the book of Luke will be revealed in the grid. As letters are filled into the grid, words there will become apparent (a black square signifies the end of a word). Fill in the letters to these words and transfer those letters to the clues below, according to the letter and the number in each square. Also, when the first letters of the answers are read top to bottom, the name of the person who spoke the quotation and the name of the quotation will be revealed.*

| J 1 | K 2 | | D 3 | I 4 | K 5 | P 6 | | L 7 | A 8 | G 9 | E 10 | | H 11 | F 12 | G 13 |
|---|---|---|---|---|---|---|---|---|---|---|---|---|---|---|---|
| C 14 | E 15 | M 16 | Q 17 | | K 18 | F 19 | G 20 | | B 21 | O 22 | F 23 | I 24 | | C 25 | J 26 |
| O 27 | | J 28 | G 29 | | C 30 | P 31 | F 32 | J 33 | E 34 | G 35 | | D 36 | N 37 | P 38 | H 39 |
| | A 40 | O 41 | B 42 | Q 43 | F 44 | K 45 | P 46 | P 47 | | D 48 | J 49 | | K 50 | B 51 | P 52 |
| | P 53 | E 54 | | L 55 | H 56 | P 57 | I 58 | Q 59 | E 60 | | A 61 | P 62 | F 63 | | C 64 |
| L 65 | | E 66 | G 67 | J 68 | H 69 | | D 70 | N 71 | | A 72 | L 73 | M 74 | M 75 | L 76 | J 77 |
| | F 78 | K 79 | E 80 | K 81 | | D 82 | I 83 | K 84 | F 85 | | L 86 | A 87 | | I 88 | P 89 |
| | E 90 | P 91 | K 92 | C 93 | F 94 | | E 95 | G 96 | M 97 | I 98 | M 99 | O 100 | | H 101 | I 102 |
| F 103 | | F 104 | K 105 | B 106 | D 107 | | M108 | C 109 | | F 110 | G 111 | J 112 | | M113 | C 114 |
| Q 115 | J 116 | | L 117 | P 118 | D 119 | | C 120 | K 121 | O 122 | | J 123 | P 124 | K 125 | O 126 | B 127 |
| | I 128 | P 129 | | A 130 | F 131 | | Q 132 | E 133 | J 134 | N 135 | | M136 | C 137 | P 138 | Q 139 |
| | O 140 | E 141 | I 142 | Q 143 | | C 144 | J 145 | H 146 | | O 147 | C 148 | A 149 | Q 150 | | J 151 |
| G152 | A 153 | P 154 | P 155 | H 156 | P 157 | G 158 | J 159 | L 160 | | F 161 | O 162 | | G 163 | F 164 | I 165 |
| P 166 | O 167 | B 168 | F 169 | N 170 | C 171 | K 172 | | | | | | | | | |

A. Large glass in the top of a car
_ _ _ _ _ _ _ _
72 87 8 153 40 130 149 61

B. "Count it ____ ..." (2 wds., James 1:2)
_ _ _ _ _ _
168 21 106 42 51 127

C. Jewish New Year (2 wds.)
_ _ _ _ _ _ _ _ _ _ _ _
148 171 109 64 144 25 30 137 114 14 93 120

D. High German language of Jewish origin
_ _ _ _ _ _ _
107 70 82 119 48 3 36

E. Gerald Ford's number (hyphenated)
_ _ _ _ _ _ _ _ _ _ _
66 133 15 60 95 54 141 34 90 10 80

F. In many places (3 wds.)
_ _ _ _ _ _ _ _ _ _ _ _ _ _ _ _
104 44 161 19 85 63 12 131 103 169 110 32 94 78 164 23

G. Number of keys on a piano (hyphenated)
_ _ _ _ _ _ _ _ _ _ _
20 111 163 67 9 29 152 158 13 96 35

H. Gandhi's first name
_ _ _ _ _ _ _
11 156 39 101 69 146 56

I. "In the year of our Lord" (2 wds., foreign)
_ _ _ _ _ _ _ _ _ _
142 165 98 4 24 83 88 58 102 128

J. Contenders for top music awards (2 wds.)
_ _ _ _ _ _ _ _ _ _ _ _ _ _
151 33 68 1 123 77 26 159 28 145 49 134 116 112

K. "Gonna find out who's ______" (3 wds.)
_ _ _ _ _ _ _ _ _ _ _ _ _
84 79 5 50 81 18 2 105 125 172 121 45 92

L. Inaugurated
_ _ _ _ _ _ _ _
73 160 55 86 117 76 65 7

M. Cagney movie, *The ______ 69th*
_ _ _ _ _ _ _ _
16 108 74 75 136 97 113 99

N. First two words of "It Might as Well Be Spring"
_ _ _ _
170 135 37 71

O. Removed from a list (2 wds.)
_ _ _ _ _ _ _ _ _ _
126 167 22 100 122 41 27 162 140 147

P. FOX TV sitcom ('03–'06, 2 wds.)
_ _ _ _ _ _ _ _
138 155 91 46 129 157 89 52

_ _ _ _ _ _ _ _ _ _ _
47 166 57 124 6 62 31 53 154 118 38

Q. Nonsense
_ _ _ _ _ _ _ _
132 59 115 150 17 143 43 139

## ONE OR THE OTHER 1

*Cross out one letter in each box so that the remaining letters will spell out a quotation from the book of Luke. A black box signifies the end of a word.*

| | | | | | | |
|---|---|---|---|---|---|---|
| W B | Y E | ■ | H L | O A | V S | T E |
| ■ | L D | I O | N R | D E | ■ | S T |
| P H | A O | N T | ■ | W T | H R | O I |
| S C | H E | ■ | H W | I A | S M | ■ |
| E O | U F | R T | ■ | E D | U A | T S |
| H Y | ■ | T S | I O | ■ | G D | O E |

______________________________

______________________________

## ADD-A-LETTER 2

*Begin with the letter shown, then add one letter at each step, rearranging the letters each time to fit the definition at the left. The last answer will be a key word from the book of Luke.*

Toward
Decay
Ripped
Ink for copiers
Type of trumpet
Thrash
Evening song in classical music
Roman leader of 100 men

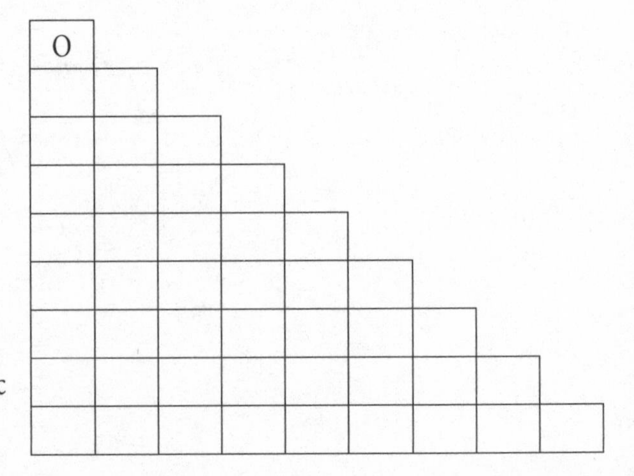

## 8 THE BARD OR THE BIBLE?

*The King James Version of the Bible was first printed in 1611, during the lifetime of William Shakespeare, who had published many of his plays by then. Readers of both will note many similarities in the grammar of the Bard of Avon and the Bible. Below are several quotations from each. Can you identify which are from Shakespeare's plays and which are from the KJV?*

1. "Neither a borrower nor a lender be." ____________________
2. "Lend, hoping for nothing again." ____________________
3. "To thine own self be true." ____________________
4. "I judge not my own self." ____________________
5. "O death, where is thy sting?" ____________________
6. "Death, a necessary end, will come when it will come." ____________________
7. "The devil can cite scripture for his purpose." ____________________
8. "… in the twinkling of an eye." ____________________
9. "They stumble that run fast." ____________________
10. "Nothing will come of nothing." ____________________
11. "A wise son maketh a glad father." ____________________
12. "It is a wise father that knows his own child." ____________________
13. "Even in laughter, the heart is sorrowful." ____________________
14. "Answer a fool according to his folly." ____________________
15. "Are you good men and true?" ____________________

## 9 THE FINAL WORD

*Fill in the missing letters to make common five-letter words below. Then transfer those letters to the corresponding numbers in the grid. Be careful; more than one letter will make a complete word, but only one letter will correctly complete the final word in the grid. The final word will be a key word from the book of Luke.*

1. T H E ___ E
2. S H A R ___
3. ___ E M O N
4. L ___ V E R
5. ___ A K E R
6. R A ___ I D
7. C R A ___ E
8. S T R ___ P
9. B ___ A R D
10. T O ___ I C

| 1 | 2 | 3 | 4 | 5 | 6 | 7 | 8 | 9 | 10 |
|---|---|---|---|---|---|---|---|---|---|
| | | | | | | | | | |

## 10 A-MAZE-ING QUOTE

*Find your way through this unique maze from start to finish by solving the clues below, whose answers comprise a quotation by Jesus from the book of Luke. The answer to each clue is a word in the quotation, given in order (clue 1 is the first word; clue 2 is the second, etc.). The number of letters in each answer has been given to help you. The quotation is hidden inside of the maze, with words in order, from start to finish. The string of words within the maze can move forward, backward, horizontally, vertically or diagonally, and even change direction within a word, but never skips a letter, nor crosses over itself.*

↓

| | | | | | | | | | | | | | | |
|---|---|---|---|---|---|---|---|---|---|---|---|---|---|---|
| G | I | V | E | X | U | N | C | E | P | L | A | D | O | P |
| B | O | S | A | R | O | T | A | R | O | R | L | A | R | O |
| Z | N | L | N | E | L | E | T | U | A | T | E | V | E | R |
| L | T | I | D | L | A | R | N | S | E | E | D | S | O | C |
| R | S | P | R | C | P | O | U | A | N | O | T | O | S | A |
| T | H | O | E | A | T | N | O | E | B | R | P | A | E | N |
| E | A | S | N | S | R | E | S | M | N | W | O | D | D | O |
| E | L | M | M | U | G | O | O | D | A | E | G | H | L | W |
| N | L | B | E | O | A | V | L | E | N | C | H | A | P | O |
| D | H | A | G | Y | N | E | K | A | D | O | N | C | U | S |
| W | E | V | I | O | T | R | I | H | S | E | R | D | N | A |
| A | N | F | T | E | H | O | G | E | T | H | A | M | L | E |
| D | U | N | R | I | B | N | U | R | D | N | I | O | P | L |
| P | R | C | O | P | I | S | N | I | N | G | O | V | E | N |
| S | O | R | E | G | O | R | A | T | O | H | R | A | S | R |

↓

1. Bestow (upon) (4) ______________
2. Also (3) ______________
3. Neutral pronoun (2) ______________
4. Will (5) ______________
5. "To ____ or not ..." (2) ______________
6. Prone (to) (5) ______________
7. To (4) ______________
8. Not me (3) ______________
9. Not bad (4) ______________
10. Find the length of (7) ______________
11. Ironed (7) ______________
12. Not up (4) ______________
13. Too (3) ______________
14. Was mixed, as dice (6) ______________
15. As one (8) ______________
16. Also (3) ______________
17. Jogging fast (7) ______________
18. Above (4) ______________

## 11 LUKE'S WHO'S WHO

*Each answer below is a name from the book of Luke. Write the name that answers each clue in the grid at left, one letter per box. When all answers have been completed correctly, the shaded column, reading down, will reveal a related quote from Luke.*

Last name of Mary (8:2)
Philip's wife, Herod's sister-in-law (3:19)
He was king when Jesus was born (1:5)
Luke's book is addressed to him (1:5)
She sat with Jesus; her sister served (10:39)
He said Jesus was "the Christ of God" (9:20)
Mother of John the Baptist (1:57)
This disciple was a publican (5:27)
Jesus was a dinner guest of this Pharisee (7:40)
He was seen in Abraham's bosom (16:20)
He was a ruler of the synagogue (8:41)
Last name of Judas (22:3)
The chief of the devils (11:15)
First person in Jesus' genealogy (3:38)
She griped about her sister to Jesus (10:38)
He was at the presentation of Jesus (1:25)
Lawgiver at Mount of Transfiguration (9:30)
He was Mary's husband (2:4)
He begged for Jesus' body (23:50)
He bore the cross of Jesus (23:26)
He sentenced Jesus to death (23:24)
Angel who announced the birth of Christ (1:26)
The father of James and John (5:10)

______________________________________________

______________________________________________

## 12 WORD LADDER 1

*Each ladder has five columns. Every answer in column A will have five letters; every answer in column B will have four; answers in column C will have three. After answering the definition for A1, drop one letter and rearrange the remaining four letters to make the answer for B1. Place the dropped letter into the box to the left of column A. Drop another letter from the B1 answer and rearrange the remaining three letters to form the answer for C1. Place the dropped letter into the box to the right of column C. Continue this pattern for the entire puzzle. When finished, the columns of dropped letters, reading down, will reveal a compound word or phrase from the book of Luke.*

| | | A | | | | | | B | | | | | C | | |
|---|---|---|---|---|---|---|---|---|---|---|---|---|---|---|---|
| 1 | | | | | | | | | | | | | | | |
| 2 | | | | | | | | | | | | | | | |
| 3 | | | | | | | | | | | | | | | |
| 4 | | | | | | | | | | | | | | | |
| 5 | | | | | | | | | | | | | | | |
| 6 | | | | | | | | | | | | | | | |
| 7 | | | | | | | | | | | | | | | |
| 8 | | | | | | | | | | | | | | | |
| 9 | | | | | | | | | | | | | | | |
| 10 | | | | | | | | | | | | | | | |
| 11 | | | | | | | | | | | | | | | |

A1. Squander
A2. Pilot
A3. Rome river
A4. Habitat
A5. Order
A6. Sedimentary rock form
A7. Valentine icon
A8. Pauses for another
A9. Trail user
A10. Provide
A11. Witch of _____

B1. Simmer
B2. Manner of living
B3. Englishman or Scot
B4. Take it on the ____
B5. Quote authoritatively
B6. Rachel's sister
B7. Tempo
B8. Senses
B9. Inheritor
B10. Sand hill
B11. Motorcycled

C1. _____ in his ways
C2. Santa's helper
C3. Adam's loss?
C4. *Monsters*, ____
C5. Frozen water
C6. Meadow
C7. Rembrandt's field
C8. Pose
C9. Him and _____
C10. Expected
C11. Mined mineral

## 13 A PROCESS OF ELIMINATION

*Follow the directions below, eliminating items from the word list. When the correct items have been removed, the remaining words, reading left to right, top to bottom, will reveal a quotation from the book of Luke.*

1. Delete all words that begin with a silent letter.
2. Delete all prepositions.
3. Delete all names of cities.
4. Delete all types of buildings.
5. Delete all shades of red.
6. Delete words that combine with the word *back* to make a compound word.
7. Delete all names of family members.
8. Delete all Old Testament books.
9. Delete all words that sound like letters.
10. Delete all metals.

| | | |
|---|---|---|
| Lead | Ruth | From |
| Jerusalem | To | Rome |
| Consider | The | Temple |
| See | Over | Judges |
| You | Are | Crimson |
| Job | Stop | Lilies |
| Silver | Knock | Numbers |
| How | Son | Upon |
| Rose | Maroon | Be |
| House | They | Bethlehem |
| Field | Grow | Father |

______________________________________________

______________________________________________

## 14 THE BAPTIZER

*The list below is a group of related words in code, where one letter stands for another. Within the same list, the code will stay the same. For example, KDBBDF could be LETTER. When you have identified a word in the list, use the solved letters to help decode other words in the same list. All of the entries in the list are from the book of Luke.*

Z H W M

________

J Y I I L S C Y V W W H I G U W H O V

____________ ________ ________ __________

N Y B V W J H B L V H I S

__________ ________________

F B L F P B L S V W L C P G

________________ ______ ______

F B L P Q W L B

________________

C Y I S L B M L O O

____________________

O H M H J R P Q W P B Y P O

______ ____ __________________

Z H B S P M B Y A L B

____________ __________

F B H F W L V

______________

F B Y O H M L B

________________

## GET OUT OF HERE!

*For each event below from the book of Luke, a list of attendees is given. One of the parties, however, was not at the event, according to Luke. Can you spot the crasher?*

1. The Birth of Christ
   Mary    Joseph    Simeon    Shepherds
2. The Presentation of Christ
   Mary    Shepherds    Simeon    Anna
3. The Miraculous Catch of Fishes
   Barnabas    Peter    James    John
4. The Calming of the Stormy Sea
   Mary    Peter    Thomas    Judas
5. The Transfiguration
   Elisha    Moses    James    John
6. The Return of the Prodigal Son
   Elder Son    Mother    Father    Servant
7. The Last Supper
   Peter    Judas    John    Pilate
8. The Trials of Jesus
   Paul    Herod    Pilate    Chief Priests
9. The Crucifixion
   Simon    Malefactors    Centurion    John the Baptist
10. The Burial and Resurrection
    Zacchaeus    Joseph    Joanna    Mary Magdalene

## ADD-A-LETTER 3

*Begin with the letter shown, then add one letter at each step, rearranging the letters each time to fit the definition at the left. The last answer will be a key word from the book of Luke.*

Not out
Whitney's cotton invention
Open smile
Rule over others
Ornamental border on cloth
From another country
"Thy sins are ______"

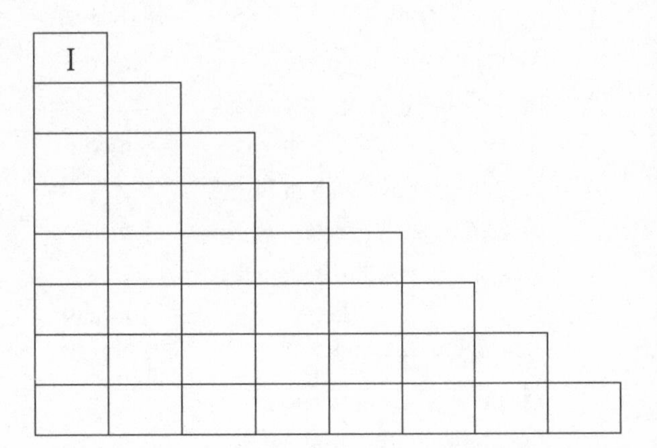


## 17 MOVIN' UP 2

*Move the letters in each column up and into the boxes above (not necessarily in the order the letters are in now) to find a quote from Jesus in the book of Luke. A block signifies the end of a word.*

| | | | | | | | | | |
|---|---|---|---|---|---|---|---|---|---|
| | | | ■ | | | | | | ■ |
| | | | | | ■ | | | | ■ |
| | | | ■ | | | | | | |
| | | | ■ | | | ■ | | | |
| A | H | A | L | F | A | E | E | A | D |
| I | H | E | | L | F | L | G | E | T |
| S | L | L | | O | L | S | S | H | |
| T | O | N | | S | | | V | O | |

## 18 HOLEY QUOTATIONS

*Below are quotations from the book of Luke with "holes"—certain letters are missing as indicated. Fill in the missing letters to complete the quotation, then rearrange those letters to spell the name of the one who spoke it.*

1. "AND THOU SHALT HOVE JOY AND OLADNOSS; AND MANY SHAOL OEJOICE AT HOS OIRTH." __ __ __ __ __ __ __
2. "OOROOALEM OHALL BE TRODDEN DOWN OF THE GENTILES." __ __ __ __ __
3. "BEHOLD THE HANDOAID OF THE LORD; BE IT UNTO ME OCCORDING TO THO WOOD." __ __ __ __
4. "DOOARO FROO MO; FOR I AM A OONFUL MAO, O LOOD." __ __ __ __ __ __ __ __ __ __
5. "LORD, DOST TOOU NOT CAOE THOT OY SISTER HOTH LEFT ME OO SERVE ALONE?" __ __ __ __ __ __
6. "OINE EYOS HAVE OEEO THY SALVATOON." __ __ __ __ __ __
7. "ART THOU ONOY A STRANGOR IN JERUSALEM, AND HAST NOT KNOWN THE THINGS WHICH ORE OOME TO OASS THERE IN THEOE DAYS?" __ __ __ __ __ __ __
8. "BOESOED ART THOU OMONG WOMEN, AND OLOSSOD OS TOE FRUIO OF THY WOMB." __ __ __ __ __ __ __ __ __
9. "IF THOU BE THE OON OF GOD, COMMOND OHIS STOOE THAT IT BE MODE BREAD." __ __ __ __ __
10. "JOHN HAVE I BEHEAOED: BUT WOO IS THIS, OF WHOM I HOAO SUCH THINGS?" __ __ __ __ __

## 19 THE STUFF PARABLES ARE MADE OF

*Luke abounds with parables, those symbolic stories that offer insightful glimpses into the kingdom of God. See how many of the characters, settings, and items from Luke's parables you can find in the grid below. Words may run forward, backward, horizontal, vertical, or diagonal.*

```
I P E E H S H I G H W A Y S P
B N G R E A T S U P P E R E R
D M U S T A R D S E E D T E O
R N F A T T E D C A L F N R D
A M U C H E L D N A C I U T I
W I D O W N V O O T W N O G G
E D R K R O E L S S A I C I A
T N C A N G E L S T I U R F L
S O B S E G D E H A C T A N S
R I A E H T F O S L W O F C O
A N A M H C I R O B H G I E N
N O B L E M A N E G D U J N A
T R O X E N I W D N A L I O N
```

| | | | |
|---|---|---|---|
| Angels | Fruits | Lost coin | Rich man |
| Barn | Good ground | Mustard seed | Rock |
| Candle | Great supper | Neighbor | Sheep |
| Far country | Hedges | Nobleman | Steward |
| Fatted calf | Highways | Oil and wine | Swine |
| Fig tree | Inn | Oxen | Thorns |
| Fowls of the air | Judge | Prodigal son | Widow |

## 20 THE BIRTH OF JOHN THE BAPTIST

*Answer these questions about the birth of John the Baptist by choosing the letter beside the correct answer. When completed, the letters of the correct answers will reveal a phrase related to John the Baptist.*

1. Who was the father of John the Baptist?
   W. Zacharias T. Abia H. Aaron
2. Who was the mother of John the Baptist?
   H. Mary E. Anna I. Elisabeth
3. What was the occupation of John the Baptist's father?
   E. Shepherd L. Priest T. Publican
4. What was John the Baptist's father supposed to do in the temple?
   O. Play a harp D. Burn incense R. Prepare a sacrifice
5. What appeared near the altar of incense?
   E. Angel N. Smoke L. Bright light
6. What did an angel predict to John the Baptist's father?
   W. Seven years of famine D. Death of Herod R. Birth of a son
7. What was Zacharias told not to let his son drink?
   N. Wine T. Goat's milk H. Water from Jacob's Well
8. When John the Baptist's father said he and his wife were too old to have children, what happened to him?
   O. Became deaf H. Became blind E. Became dumb
9. Who predicted John the Baptist's birth to his father?
   E. Michael W. Jesus S. Gabriel
10. When John the Baptist's mother knew she was with child, how long did she hide herself?
    M. Five days S. Five months A. Five weeks
11. Who was Elisabeth's cousin, also visited by an angel?
    V. Mary S. Peter T. Martha
12. How long did Mary visit Elizabeth?
    P. Three days O. Three months H. Three weeks
13. When John the Baptist was 8 days old, what name was suggested for him?
    I. Zacharias A. Isaac E. Abia
14. How did John the Baptist's father let it be known that his son's name would be John?
    S. Spoke it C. Wrote it T. Signed it
15. What did John the Baptist's father do immediately after he gave his son's name?
    S. He died E. He spoke H. He offered a sacrifice

________________________________________

## 21 QUOTATION CODES

*Each numbered puzzle below is a quotation of Jesus in code. Each puzzle has its own code: one letter stands for another letter, always the same one within each puzzle. When you have identified a word in the quotation, use the solved letters to help decode other words in the same quotation. For example, KDBBDF could be LETTER.*

1.

K O X B I L G X I Y X C G L X F X I X I F F

____ ___ ____ _______ ____

B O X I F B O F P I F F D B A A F Q

__ ___ ___ _____ _____

N T C B X I F B X I F Q.

____ ___ _____

2.

M O B Z Q C D J B J N P A D J M O S D T

___ _______ __ ______ __

O N P O N J B.

___ ____

3.

A O K P C D K C M G L Z K A O N I

___ ____ __ ____ ____

G K N A N I R A O K T L R E C M G L Z K

____ ___ ___ ____ __ ____

A O N I Z N C G K I A.

____ _______

4.

R W Y W H S B Y O R R S C D Q N O M S Y H R

___ _______ _____ __ _____

P C R R W Y D H P A S Y S O H S Y T Y E.

___ ___ ________ ___ ___

5.

Y B C   Y L F   M G   B D Y O O   E N   W M X N L

___ ___ __ _____ __ _____

H A T,   B N N C   Y L F   H N   B D Y O O   P M L F,

___ ____ ___ __ _____ ____

C L A Q C   Y L F   M G   B D Y O O   E N

_____ ___ __ _____ __

A Z N L N F   T L G A   H A T.

______ ____ ___

## 22 LOST COIN

*In Luke 15, Jesus spoke of a woman who had ten coins, but lost one. She searched diligently, using the extra light of a candle, and sweeping the house until she found it. Then she called her neighbors over to celebrate. Can you help her find it? In the puzzle below, the word "coin" appears only once. The word may be forward, backward, diagonal, vertical, or horizontal. Find it; then invite some friends over.*

O I N C I N I C O N I O N O C
I N O C O I M I C O N N I C O
I O N O O N C O N I C O L N I
N I O O I I O C O N I C O I M
C C I C O N O I O I C M O I C
O I N O I C O I O N O O I N I
I N O M I O C N N O I N I O N
O N I O N C I O N C M O I L C
N O I C O I C I N O C O N I C
C N I O N I C C O I C N C O N
O C I C O N I O N C I O N O C
N I C O N I C O O N C O I C N
I N N C I O N C C O N I O M O
C I C O N O C I O N N M I O C
I O N C N O I C C I O N N I I

## 23 WORD ADDITION

*Begin with the word in the first column. Add one letter to it and rearrange all of the letters to form a word that answers the clue at the right. Write the additional letter on the first blank and the new word on the second blank. When all of the first-blank correct letters have been filled in, a quotation of Jesus from the book of Luke will be revealed, reading top to bottom.*

| | | | | | | |
|---|---|---|---|---|---|---|
| 1. | TIRES | + | ____ | = | ____________ | The temple had a high one |
| 2. | SASH | + | ____ | = | ____________ | Leftovers from a barbecue |
| 3. | MINER | + | ____ | = | ____________ | Stay |
| 4. | SHONE | + | ____ | = | ____________ | Selected |
| 5. | PRAY | + | ____ | = | ____________ | Return a favor |
| 6. | SATE | + | ____ | = | ____________ | Beauty's partner |
| 7. | CAPE | + | ____ | = | ____________ | Serenity |
| 8. | FEAR | + | ____ | = | ____________ | "… Jill came tumbling ______" |
| 9. | TUBA | + | ____ | = | ____________ | Regarding |
| 10. | LEANER | + | ____ | = | ____________ | ______ flame |
| 11. | STARVE | + | ____ | = | ____________ | Fall event |
| 12. | CANTER | + | ____ | = | ____________ | Sure |
| 13. | TIERS | + | ____ | = | ____________ | Mother Theresa was one, once |
| 14. | RATE | + | ____ | = | ____________ | E.T. "phoned home" from here |
| 15. | DOTS | + | ____ | = | ____________ | "______ Up" (1957 Ricky Nelson hit) |
| 16. | SHOE | + | ____ | = | ____________ | Often a winner in Vegas |
| 17. | PURE | + | ____ | = | ____________ | Word before "Mario Brothers" |
| 18. | RENT | + | ____ | = | ____________ | Sign on opposite side of exit door |

________________________________________________

________________________________________________

## ADD-A-LETTER 4

*Begin with the letter shown, then add one letter at each step, rearranging the letters each time to fit the definition at the left. The last answer will be a key word from the book of Luke.*

| | | | | | | | | |
|---|---|---|---|---|---|---|---|---|
| | A | | | | | | | |
| Ma's better half | | | | | | | | |
| Mimic | | | | | | | | |
| Bosc is one variety of it | | | | | | | | |
| Adorn with folds of cloth | | | | | | | | |
| Got the ten pin, maybe | | | | | | | | |
| Lose hope | | | | | | | | |
| "Today shalt thou be with me in ______" | | | | | | | | |

## 25 MOVIN' UP 3

*Move the letters in each column up and into the boxes above (not necessarily in the order the letters are in now) to find a quote from Jesus in the book of Luke. A block signifies the end of a word.*

| | | | | | | | | | | | | | |
|---|---|---|---|---|---|---|---|---|---|---|---|---|---|
| | | | | ■ | | | ■ | | ■ | | | | ■ |
| | | | | | | | | | | ■ | | | ■ |
| | | ■ | | | | | ■ | | | | ■ | | |
| | | | ■ | | | | | | ■ | | | | ■ |
| | | | | ■ | | | | | | | | ■ | ■ |

| | | | | | | | | | | | | | |
|---|---|---|---|---|---|---|---|---|---|---|---|---|---|
| A | D | A | A | A | H | A | G | A | D | A | A | D | H |
| H | E | E | E | N | I | I | L | D | E | E | I | F | |
| L | H | S | G | W | I | N | M | E | H | L | F | N | |
| O | L | V | T | | O | R | | S | | M | N | W | |
| W | O | | | | T | S | | T | | | | | |

## 26 RED-LETTER EDITION

*Write the answer that completes each clue in the grid to the right, one letter to each box. All of the phrases are from sayings of Jesus in the book of Luke. When each answer is correctly filled in, the first column, reading down, will reveal a quotation from Luke that fits the theme of this puzzle. The Scripture reference from Luke for each clue is given in parentheses.*

"Physician, _____ thyself ..." (4:23)

"Launch out _____ the deep ..." (5:4)

"... many _____ come in my name ..." (21:8)

"_____ is your faith?" (8:25)

"... accounted worthy to _____ that world ..." (20:35)

"_____ therefore unto Caesar ..." (20:25)

"Simon,... Satan hath _____ to have you ..." (22:31)

"... I sent you _____ purse and scrip ..." (22:35)

"Watch ye therefore, and pray _____ ..." (21:36)

"... upon whom the tower in _____ fell ..." (13:4)

"Her sins, _____ are many, are forgiven ..." (7:47)

"... your _____ part is full of ... wickedness ..." (11:39)

"Thou shalt not _____ the Lord ..." (4:12)

"... and the ruin of that _____ was great." (6:49)

"... in _____, that seeing they might not see ..." (8:10)

"... hold to the one, and despise the _____." (16:13)

"They that are _____ need not a physician ..." (5:31)

"Give to _____ man that asketh of thee ..." (6:30)

"I came not to call the _____ ..." (5:32)

| | | | | | | | | |
|---|---|---|---|---|---|---|---|---|
| | | | | | | | | |
| | | | | | | | | |
| | | | | | | | | |
| | | | | | | | | |
| | | | | | | | | |
| | | | | | | | | |
| | | | | | | | | |
| | | | | | | | | |
| | | | | | | | | |
| | | | | | | | | |
| | | | | | | | | |
| | | | | | | | | |
| | | | | | | | | |
| | | | | | | | | |
| | | | | | | | | |
| | | | | | | | | |
| | | | | | | | | |
| | | | | | | | | |
| | | | | | | | | |

_______________________________________________

_______________________________________________

## 27 WORD LADDER 2

*Each ladder has five columns. Every answer in column A will have five letters; every answer in column B will have four; answers in column C will have three. After answering the definition for A1, drop one letter and rearrange the remaining four letters to make the answer for B1. Place the dropped letter into the box to the left of column A. Drop another letter from the B1 answer and rearrange the remaining three letters to form the answer for C1. Place the dropped letter into the box to the right of column C. Continue this pattern for the entire puzzle. When finished, the columns of dropped letters, reading down, will reveal a compound word or phrase from the book of Luke.*

| | | A | | | | | B | | | | C | | | |
|---|---|---|---|---|---|---|---|---|---|---|---|---|---|---|
| 1 | | | | | | | | | | | | | | |
| 2 | | | | | | | | | | | | | | |
| 3 | | | | | | | | | | | | | | |
| 4 | | | | | | | | | | | | | | |
| 5 | | | | | | | | | | | | | | |
| 6 | | | | | | | | | | | | | | |
| 7 | | | | | | | | | | | | | | |

A1. ______ Room
A2. Café
A3. Sample a dish
A4. ______ Polo
A5. Hinder
A6. Mechanical worker
A7. Evade

B1. Undefiled
B2. Peeling
B3. Try
B4. Wander
B5. _____ *and the Tramp*
B6. Cheer
B7. Combat for two

C1. Each
C2. Unburden
C3. Collection
C4. Blemish
C5. Boy
C6. Decay
C7. Guided

## 28 INITIAL CHANGES

Replace the first letter of each word below to make another word that will complete the verse from the book of Luke. No letters or words have to be rearranged.

CAN WHALL GOT GIVE MY DREAD CLONE

_______________________________________________

## 29 SCAVENGER HUNT

*Can you find:*

1. An NFL team in Luke 12:24________________________
2. A TV game show in Luke 8:23________________________
3. A Cub Scout group in Luke 19:46 ________________________
4. A bottom line in Luke 5:6 ________________________
5. Any digits in Luke 11:46 ________________________
6. A bolt without a nut in Luke 17:24 ________________________
7. Parts of a yard in Luke 7:44 ________________________
8. A TV network in Luke 13:32 ________________________
9. An itemized list in Luke 16:6 ________________________
10. A keyboard word in Luke 7:6________________________
11. A place for a potato in Luke 5:19 ________________________
12. A sticker in Luke 18:25 ________________________
13. A palindrome in Luke 2:36 ________________________
14. A magazine in Luke 9:51 ________________________
15. A sweetheart in Luke 16:24 ________________________
16. A young whale in Luke 15:23________________________
17. A pizza topper in Luke 19:29________________________
18. An alley pickup in Luke 15:17 ________________________
19. A tennis game opener in Luke 10:40 ________________________
20. A boxing venue in Luke 15:22 ________________________

## 30 THE LAST SUPPER

*The list below is a group of related words in code, where one letter stands for another. Within the same list, the code will stay the same. For example, KDBBDF could be LETTER. When you have identified a word in the list, use the solved letters to help decode other words in the same list. All of the entries in the list are from the book of Luke.*

V P Y Y D M Q F

________

Z V V Q F F D D B

_____ ____

H C L F H Q Q U B Q U

_______ ___

N Z V

___

E F Z L H D E H C Q M L U Q

_____ __ ___ ____

Z U T Q P M Q U Q G R F Q P G

_________ _____

H O D Y O D F G Y

___ ______

V L H N C Q F D E O P H Q F

_______ __ _____

H C P U J Y S L M L U S

____________

H C L Y G D L U F Q B Q B R F P U N Q D E B Q

____ __ __ ___________ __ __

## ONE OR THE OTHER 2

*Cross out one letter in each box so that the remaining letters will spell out a quotation from the book of Luke. A black box signifies the end of a word.*

| A / T | H / R | E / Y | ■ | R / L | I / O | V / G | H / E |
|---|---|---|---|---|---|---|---|
| S / T | ■ | O / T | O / F | ■ | F / T | H / O | R / E |
| ■ | M / B | A / O | D / N | Y / E | ■ | A / I | S / T |
| ■ | D / T | I / H | O / E | ■ | E / B | A / Y | E / D |

______________________________

## 32 LEFT HAND, RIGHT HAND

*Use the letters below to compete a familiar 13-word verse from the book of Luke. The letters are in the correct order (without the spaces), but are divided into two groups, according to which hand is used to type them on a keyboard. Beginning with the left hand, put the words together again, adding spaces properly, to complete the verse.*

Left Hand

T E T A T A R E W E E E D T A S C A B T T E T A T A R E S C

Right Hand

H Y H H O L N N O P H Y I I N U H Y H I K

______________________________

______________________________

______________________________

## 33 WORD LADDER 3

*Each ladder has five columns. Every answer in column A will have five letters; every answer in column B will have four; answers in column C will have three. After answering the definition for A1, drop one letter and rearrange the remaining four letters to make the answer for B1. Place the dropped letter into the box to the left of column A. Drop another letter from the B1 answer and rearrange the remaining three letters to form the answer for C1. Place the dropped letter into the box to the right of column C. Continue this pattern for the entire puzzle. When finished, the columns of dropped letters, reading down, will reveal a compound word or phrase from the book of Luke.*

| | | A | | | | | B | | | | C | | | |
|---|---|---|---|---|---|---|---|---|---|---|---|---|---|---|
| 1 | | | | | | | | | | | | | | |
| 2 | | | | | | | | | | | | | | |
| 3 | | | | | | | | | | | | | | |
| 4 | | | | | | | | | | | | | | |
| 5 | | | | | | | | | | | | | | |
| 6 | | | | | | | | | | | | | | |
| 7 | | | | | | | | | | | | | | |
| 8 | | | | | | | | | | | | | | |

A1. Team race
A2. Designated path
A3. Hams or steaks
A4. Support for artist's canvas
A5. Caprices
A6. Thread
A7. Put off
A8. Royal

B1. Ivy League school
B2. ______ de France
B3. Orient
B4. Make secure
B5. Hope for
B6. Flame
B7. Allen or Flintstone
B8. Strong wind

C1. Positive vote
C2. Deep tire track
C3. Ionian ______
C4. Meadow
C5. Belonging to him
C6. Umpire
C7. Crimson
C8. Fall behind

## 34 SHADY COLUMNS

*Place the six-letter answer of each clue in the boxes at the right. When all correct answers have been placed, the shaded columns, reading top to bottom, will reveal a quotation of Jesus from the book of Luke.*

1. Small hole for a shoelace
2. Area in front of a fireplace
3. A yellow tropical fruit
4. Parentless child
5. Discarded ship cargo
6. Godzilla's nemesis in '64 flick
7. Crocheted blanket
8. _______ Bear
9. Full of pores
10. Mature (2 words)
11. Snaky-haired woman of mythology
12. One who avoids the subject
13. ______ Knows Best ('54-'60 TV series)
14. Best friend of Nancy in comic strip
15. Trench made by a plow
16. Matt Dillon's deputy Haggen

|   |   |   |   |   |   |
|---|---|---|---|---|---|
|   |   |   |   |   |   |
|   |   |   |   |   |   |
|   |   |   |   |   |   |
|   |   |   |   |   |   |
|   |   |   |   |   |   |
|   |   |   |   |   |   |
|   |   |   |   |   |   |
|   |   |   |   |   |   |
|   |   |   |   |   |   |
|   |   |   |   |   |   |
|   |   |   |   |   |   |
|   |   |   |   |   |   |
|   |   |   |   |   |   |
|   |   |   |   |   |   |
|   |   |   |   |   |   |
|   |   |   |   |   |   |

______________________________________________

______________________________________________

## 35 SIGNS OF THE SECOND COMING

*The list below is a group of related words in code, where one letter stands for another. Within the same list, the code will stay the same. For example, KDBBDF could be LETTER. When you have identified a word in the list, use the solved letters to help decode other words in the same list. All of the entries in the list are from the book of Luke.*

D P X

___

R P X U F I A P Y R B

___________

N P Z E O R

______

K R B U E H R O L R

__________

N P Z E H V Q R U X P V P H B

______ _________

P X Z E R B E O S R X A B P H R Z

______ __ _________

M P V B G N J R O T R P O L R

____ __ _________

M E B U X R B B G N O P U E G O B

________ __ _______

X G P X E O T B R P

_______ ___

B E T O B E O U F R B A O P O M Z G G O

_____ __ ___ ___ ___ ____

## 36 LEFTOVERS

*Answer the quiz questions below. The answers may be found in the list of words, though not necessarily in order. Cross off each answer from the list. The remaining words, when read left to right, top to bottom, will reveal a quotation from the book of Luke.*

| | | | | |
|---|---|---|---|---|
| give | the | centurion | send | love |
| an | temple | is | where | this |
| your | angel | tempt | two | enemies |

1. Of whom did Jesus say, "I have not found so great faith, no, not in Israel"? (7:9)
2. The disciples told Jesus to "_________ the multitude away" (9:12).
3. At the end of Luke, where were the disciples? (24:53)
4. A voice said, "_________ is my beloved Son: hear him" (9:35).
5. What did Zacharias see on the right side of the altar of incense? (1:11)
6. Jesus said, "Thou shalt not _________ the Lord thy God (4:12).
7. "And he said unto them, "_________ is your faith?" (8:25).
8. How many sons did the father of the prodigal son have? (15:11)
9. "_________ to every man that asketh of thee" (6:30).
10. "This _________ my body which is given for you" (22:19).
11. "The Son of man cometh at _________ hour when ye think not" (12:40).
12. "...for so did their fathers to _________ false prophets" (6:26).

___

___

## 37 KNOCKOUTS

*Below is a quotation of Jesus from the book of Luke. All of the words are there, in the correct order, with the letters in correct order as well, but one letter has been added to each word. "Knock out" the unnecessary letter in each word to reveal the quotation.*

THOUS PART MAY BELOSVED SION;
SIN THERE IN ATM WEALL PLEASTED

___

___

## 38 SIX BY SIX

*Each answer that completes the phrases below from the book of Luke can be found in the grid, reading in any direction. Each answer is six letters long, beginning along one of the outside edges, and ending at the opposite outside edge. The letters of each answer must always be next to each other, but the direction may move diagonally within each word. Every letter within the grid will be used, some more than once.*

1. "Woman, thou art ___ ___ ___ ___ ___ ___" (13:12).
2. "He took the five ___ ___ ___ ___ ___ ___ and the two fishes" (9:16).
3. "The babe ___ ___ ___ ___ ___ ___ in her womb" (1:41).
4. "He said unto him, '___ ___ ___ ___ ___ ___ me'" (5:27).
5. "He called his ___ ___ ___ ___ ___ ___ disciples together" (9:1).
6. "He went into the ___ ___ ___ ___ ___ ___ of the Lord" (1:9).
7. "Beware ye of the ___ ___ ___ ___ ___ ___ of the Pharisees" (12:1).
8. "___ ___ ___ ___ ___ ___ is justified of all her children" (7:35).
9. "Consider the ___ ___ ___ ___ ___ ___ how they grow" (12:27).

| | | | | | |
|---|---|---|---|---|---|
| N | D | L | E | W | L |
| E | V | E | I | O | T |
| P | V | S | L | A | E |
| A | D | O | I | L | V |
| T | E | O | P | E | O |
| L | E | M | L | S | F |

## 39 SYLLABLE BY SYLLABLE

*Answer each definition below by putting together the syllables from the box at the top, one letter for each blank. The number in parentheses indicates the number of syllables in that answer. When all of the answers are filled in properly, a quotation of Jesus from the book of Luke can be found by reading the first and last letters of the answers top to bottom.*

A A A AGE AH AL AL AN AN ANS AS BE BI CAR CUL DA DAL DAM DE DI DI DOME E E FLOR FRONT FRUT GRO GULF HAM HAR HEZ HOM HOO HOU I I I I IM IN IN IS JAMES KEYS KI LA LE LET LI LI LIEF LO LU LU NA NA NAI NI NI ON OT PORCH POT PROMP QUI RA RY SA SAC SCAN SI TEA THES TI TI TI TIAL TRAIN TRIV TU TUT UN VER VO WAG

1. Famous escape artist (3) __________
2. "Elijah" in the New Testament (3) _______
3. Of little significance (3) __________
4. Tribute (2) _________
5. Priscilla's husband (3) _________
6. Recipients of at least two epistles (5) ____________________
7. Surname of Jesus' betrayer (4) ____________
8. Saudi Arabian peninsula (2) _______
9. Southeastern US archipelago (2 wds.) (4) _________________
10. Sea between Saudi Arabia and Iran (2 wds.) (5) _________________
11. Hoosier state (4) __________
12. City of central Italy (3) _________
13. He said, "To be or not to be" (2) _________
14. Andy and Aunt Bee often sat here (2 wds.) (2) _______________

15. Lack of faith (3)____________
16. Humdinger (2)_____
17. First letter of any name (3)__________
18. Peter Pan pooch (2)_____
19. Harding administration cover up (3 wds.) (5)__________________________
20. Famous big band trumpeter (2 wds.) (3)_______________
21. Lively musical direction (3)__________
22. Many-fruited ice cream flavor (2 wds., hyphenated) (4)_________________
23. TV Western series (2 wds.) (3)_______________
24. River-stopper south of Las Vegas (2 wds.) (3)______________
25. Spur-of-the-moment (3)______________
26. Neighborhood dead-end street (hyphenated) (3)____________
27. King of Judah granted 15 extra years of life (4)____________

## ONE OR THE OTHER 3

*Cross out one letter in each box so that the remaining letters will spell out a quotation from the book of Luke. A black box signifies the end of a word.*

| | | | | | | | |
|---|---|---|---|---|---|---|---|
| S T | L H | Y E | ■ | S K | I E | L N | G L |
| E D | O R | S M | ■ | O T | O F | ■ | G Y |
| E O | U D | ■ | I A | S T | ■ | W B | I R |
| I T | H T | I E | N R | ■ | M Y | O A | U N |

___________________________________________

# THE GOSPEL ACCORDING TO ST. JOHN

## SCAVENGER HUNT

*Can you find:*

1. Modeling material in 9:15 ______
2. A musical combo in 18:3 ______
3. A Denzel Washington movie in 17:22 ______
4. A plastics company in 8:56 ______
5. Potato features in 9:30 ______
6. A vacation destination in 18:20 ______
7. Bees and tees in 7:15 ______
8. An Old Testament book in 16:25 ______
9. A date maker in 12:13 ______
10. A group of students in 19:38 ______
11. A Motown group in 6:26 ______
12. A tributary in 15:4 ______
13. An LP in 12:17 ______
14. A tie in 4:11 ______
15. A cover in 16:7 ______
16. Music of the people in 5:3 ______
17. A low tennis score in 13:34 ______
18. A comic creator in 5:28 ______
19. A birthday item in 14:25 ______
20. A mail order fee in 6:24 ______

## 2 WORD LADDER 1

*Each ladder has five columns. Every answer in column A will have five letters; every answer in column B will have four; answers in column C will have three. After answering the definition for A1, drop one letter and rearrange the remaining four letters to make the answer for B1. Place the dropped letter into the box to the left of column A. Drop another letter from the B1 answer and rearrange the remaining three letters to form the answer for C1. Place the dropped letter into the box to the right of column C. Continue this pattern for the entire puzzle. When finished, the columns of dropped letters, reading down, will reveal a phrase from the book of John.*

| | | A | | | | | B | | | | C | | | |
|---|---|---|---|---|---|---|---|---|---|---|---|---|---|---|
| 1 | | | | | | | | | | | | | | |
| 2 | | | | | | | | | | | | | | |
| 3 | | | | | | | | | | | | | | |
| 4 | | | | | | | | | | | | | | |
| 5 | | | | | | | | | | | | | | |
| 6 | | | | | | | | | | | | | | |

A1. Fence openings
A2. Verdi work
A3. "Unholey"
A4. Lift
A5. Blot
A6. Inflate

B1. Recliner, for one
B2. Harvest
B3. Superman's gal
B4. Corn units
B5. Louise or Turner
B6. Stain

C1. Consumed
C2. Exist
C3. "O ______ Mio"
C4. Sargasso ______
C5. Beige
C6. Volley

## 3 ADD-A-LETTER 1

*Begin with the letter shown, then add one letter at each step, rearranging the letters each time to fit the definition at the right. The last answer will be a key word from the book of John.*

Gangster Barker
Spoil
St. Louis NFL team
Wanders
Pilate, Herod and Caesar

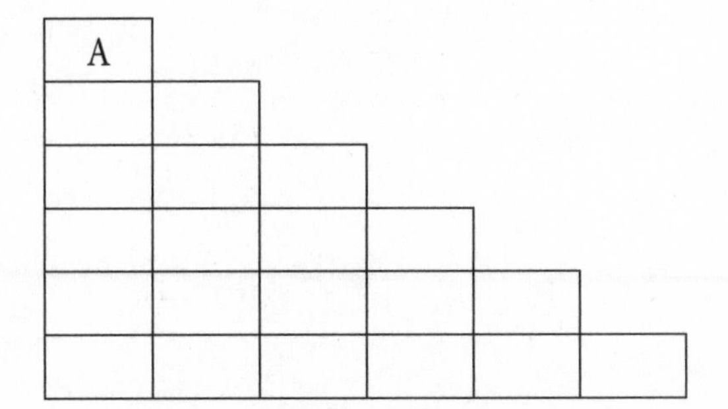

## 4 JOHN WHO?

*John, the disciple and inner-circle friend of Jesus, is one of the most famous persons named John in history, but there are many others, real and fictional. Can you match the famous "John" to his or her claim to fame?*

1. Second president of the United States ______
2. Robin Hood's sidekick ______
3. Academy Award-winning film composer ______
4. Composer of "Amazing Grace" ______
5. Former quarterback for the Denver Broncos ______
6. Academy Award-winning western actor ______
7. The forerunner of Jesus Christ ______
8. Early explorer whose life was saved by Pocahontas ______
9. Tenth president of the United States ______
10. Four-time Academy Award-winning director ______
11. Composer of "Annie's Song" ______
12. Sixth president of the United States ______
13. Author of *Paradise Lost* ______
14. Shirley Temple's first husband and costar in *She Wore a Yellow Ribbon* ______
15. Tobacco planter and husband of Pocahontas ______
16. Thirty-fifth president of the United States ______
17. Winner of seven Grand Slam singles titles ______
18. Four-time Grammy Award-winning singer ______
19. Sherlock Holmes's sidekick ______
20. First American to orbit the earth ______

a. John Tyler
b. John Elway
c. John Glenn
d. John Adams
e. John Milton
f. John McEnroe
g. John Smith
h. John Wayne
i. John Williams
j. Little John
k. John the Baptist
l. John Watson
m. John Agar
n. John Q. Adams
o. John Denver
p. John Newton
q. Olivia Newton-John
r. John F. Kennedy
s. John Ford
t. John Rolfe

## 5 SHADY COLUMNS

*Place the six-letter answer of each clue in the boxes at the right. When all correct answers have been placed, the shaded columns, reading top to bottom, will reveal a quotation of Jesus from the book of John.*

1. Solomon was known for his
2. Crude image of hated person
3. Enigmatic or mysterious
4. Gasoline company with big red star
5. Olympic skiing event
6. Prison of Johnny Cash blues song
7. Donald Trump's daughter
8. Actor Jack of *Some Like It Hot*
9. Infused
10. Medieval manuscript medium
11. City north of Chicago
12. Jesus is the "______ for the season"
13. Muppet frog
14. *Wide World of* ______

______________________________

______________________________

## 6 ADD-A-LETTER 2

*Begin with the letter shown, then add one letter at each step, rearranging the letters each time to fit the definition at the right. The last answer will be a key word from the book of John.*

I

Exists

Knighthood title

Mix

Vacations

Holy ________

## 7 A-MAZE-ING QUOTE

*Find your way through this unique maze from start to finish by solving the clues below, whose answers comprise a quotation by Jesus from the book of John. The answer to each clue is a word in the quotation, given in order (clue 1 is the first word; clue 2 is the second, etc.). The number of letters in each answer has been given to help you. The quotation is hidden inside of the maze, with words in order, from start to finish. The string of words within the maze can move forward, backward, horizontally, vertically, or diagonally, but never skips a letter, nor crosses over itself.*

↓

| I | G | I | V | E | F | R | O | M | P | E | R | I | S | H |
|---|---|---|---|---|---|---|---|---|---|---|---|---|---|---|
| T | E | S | P | U | L | L | E | Y | R | A | T | C | E | N |
| E | A | D | S | N | N | O | A | E | A | S | N | A | E | O |
| R | N | E | E | T | T | D | V | N | Y | O | L | I | D | N |
| G | V | T | R | O | O | E | E | E | R | A | T | L | C | E |
| E | M | E | H | T | N | E | A | R | L | H | U | A | E | K |
| T | L | R | R | L | O | O | T | O | E | O | E | E | C | T |
| E | N | A | N | L | V | U | O | R | H | V | N | U | H | A |
| R | I | A | N | A | I | H | G | S | A | K | L | E | R | R |
| N | O | A | H | H | C | U | N | H | L | P | M | U | E | R |
| A | E | G | Y | S | O | E | A | A | U | N | O | S | M | Y |
| L | L | R | E | Y | E | H | T | L | O | A | U | X | F | H |
| O | E | I | A | R | K | E | D | L | S | M | T | O | E | A |
| V | O | L | F | I | S | N | I | A | N | Y | O | R | D | N |
| E | E | I | D | E | A | R | E | C | E | D | N | W | E | D |

↓

1. Myself (1) ____
2. Grant (4) ____
3. Until (4) ____
4. Those guys (4) ____
5. Everlasting (7) ____
6. Popular Hasbro® board game (4) ____
7. Plus (3) ____
8. Third person plural pronoun (4) ____
9. Will (5) ____
10. No way (5) ____
11. Decay (6) ____
12. Nor (7) ____
13. "____ We Dance?" (5) ____
14. Whatever one (3) ____
15. Adam was one (3) ____
16. Sharp tug (5) ____
17. 1954 sci-fi classic (4) ____
18. One of 6 in an inning (3) ____
19. A preposition (2) ____
20. Mine (2) ____
21. Cards dealt to player (4) ____

## 8 KNOCKOUTS

*Below are quotations of Jesus from the book of John. All of the words are there, in the correct order, with the letters in correct order as well, but one letter has been added to each word. "Knock out" the unnecessary letter in each word to reveal each quotation.*

1. IS HAM THEY TRUCE VEINE

______________________________

2. SHE HIS AM LIARD CAND THEN FRATHER ORF INT

______________________________

3. INT ITS IN; BEY NOWT AFRANID

______________________________

4. BYE MAUST BEG BOREN ARGAIN

______________________________

5. OIF MANY MEAN THIRSTY LEST HISM COAME UINTO MYE FAND DRAINK

______________________________

## ONE OR THE OTHER 1

*Cross out one letter in each box so that the remaining letters will spell out a quotation from the book of John. A black box signifies the end of a word.*

| | | | | | | | | | |
|---|---|---|---|---|---|---|---|---|---|
| A I | F S | ■ | W T | H R | I A | S T | ■ | C M | E A |
| N T | ■ | W B | E H | E R | E N | ■ | A N | N O | D T |
| ■ | O I | N F | ■ | N G | E O | D T | ■ | H O | E H |
| ■ | C W | H O | U I | L N | E D | ■ | T D | O A | ■ |
| N B | E O | T W | H E | E I | N D | E G | ■ | ■ | ■ |

## 10 SYLLABLE BY SYLLABLE

*Answer each definition below by putting together the syllables from the box at the top, one letter for each blank. The number in parentheses indicates the number of syllables in that answer. When all of the answers are completed, a quotation of Jesus from the book of John can be found by reading the first and last letters of the answers top to bottom.*

A AL AP BO BUK CA DIG DOOR DRUM EAR ED
ED EL EN ER ER EV EY EY GA GOOS GREEN
HA HAR HITH HO IN IN KIS LE LIAM LIGHT
LIKE LIL LIM LIS LOOS LOW LU LU MA MET
NA NAC NESS NO NO OP PE ROCK RY STONE
TELL TIM TION TITE TO TO TU TWI VAN VEL
VOL WANT WEISS WIL YEL ZONE

1. Legendary Swiss archer (2 wds.) (3) _ _ _ _ _ _ _ _ _ _ _ _ _ _
2. Preference (3) _ _ _ _ _ _ _ _ _ _
3. Image (2) _ _ _ _ _ _ _ _ _ _
4. Fate (2) _ _ _ _ _ _ _
5. ’54 Como hit (2) _ _ _ _ _ _ _
6. Cuban capital (3) _ _ _ _ _ _ _
7. Related to a building’s interior (2) _ _ _ _ _ _ _
8. ’63 Checker hit (2 wds.) (3) _ _ _ _ _ _ _ _ _ _ _ _
9. Always fresh (3) _ _ _ _ _ _ _ _ _ _ _ _
10. World’s first national park (3) _ _ _ _ _ _ _ _ _ _ _ _ _ _
11. Alpine perennial (3) _ _ _ _ _ _ _ _ _ _ _ _
12. Bing Crosby’s given names (2 wds.) (4) _ _ _ _ _ _ _ _ _ _ _ _ _ _
13. *The Farmer’s* ______ (3) _ _ _ _ _ _ _ _ _
14. Vesuvius, for one (3) _ _ _ _ _ _ _ _ _
15. Tympanic membrane (2) _ _ _ _ _ _ _ _ _
16. Classic TV anthology series (2 wds.) (3) _ _ _ _ _ _ _ _ _ _ _ _ _ _ _
17. 50th state capital (4) _ _ _ _ _ _ _ _ _ _

18. Wrap completely (3) _ _ _ _ _ _ _ _ _

19. Musical direction for smoothly (3) _ _ _ _ _ _ _

20. Anger caused by unfairness (4) _ _ _ _ _ _ _ _ _ _ _ _ _ _

21. Friend of Henny Penny (2 wds.) (4) _ _ _ _ _ _ _ _ _ _ _ _ _ _ _ _

22. Up till now (3) _ _ _ _ _ _ _ _ _ _

23. Famed West African town (3) _ _ _ _ _ _ _ _ _ _

## 11 MOVIN' UP 1

*Move the letters in each column up and into the boxes above (not necessarily in the order the letters are in now) to find a quote from Jesus in the book of John. A block signifies the end of a word.*

| | | | | | | | | | |
|---|---|---|---|---|---|---|---|---|---|
| | | ■ | | | ■ | | | | |
| | ■ | | | | ■ | | | | |
| | | | | ■ | | | ■ | | |
| ■ | | | | | ■ | | ■ | | |
| | | ■ | | | ■ | | | ■ | ■ |
| H | F | A | D | E | I | A | H | A | I |
| I | I | A | G | E | | I | N | M | L |
| L | L | N | M | K | | I | T | W | T |
| L | N | | S | O | | N | | Y | Y |
| | | | Y | | | S | | | |

## 12 ACROSTIC

*Answer each clue, then transfer the letters from the blanks to the grid according to the number under each blank. A quotation from the book of John will be revealed in the grid. As letters are filled into the grid, words there will become apparent (a black square signifies the end of a word). Fill in the letters to these words and transfer those letters to the clues below, according to the letter and the number in each square. Also, when the first letters of the answers are read top to bottom, the location of the quotation in the book of John will be revealed.*

| H 1 | M 2 | E 3 | | A 4 | I 5 | O 6 | | K 7 | Q 8 | E 9 | D 10 | | D 11 | K 12 |
|---|---|---|---|---|---|---|---|---|---|---|---|---|---|---|
| A 13 | F 14 | A 15 | | F 16 | K 17 | | E 18 | M 19 | P 20 | A 21 | L 22 | J 23 | O 24 | F 25 |
| | K 26 | K 27 | | L 28 | O 29 | B 30 | D 31 | G 32 | F 33 | D 34 | | D 35 | K 36 | |
| C 37 | B 38 | P 39 | | P 40 | I 41 | E 42 | B 43 | K 44 | M 45 | J 46 | | L 47 | J 48 | C 49 |
| Q 50 | | P 51 | J 52 | | M 53 | M 54 | | B 55 | A 56 | | N 57 | A 58 | | A 59 |
| L 60 | N 61 | O 62 | F 63 | M 64 | J 65 | | A 66 | N 67 | E 68 | K 69 | M 70 | | G 71 | I 72 |
| O 73 | | G 74 | N 75 | K 76 | F 77 | | E 78 | C 79 | M 80 | H 81 | A 82 | Q 83 | I 84 | P 85 |
| | P 86 | D 87 | | H 88 | O 89 | | P 90 | H 91 | N 92 | G 93 | | H 94 | I 95 | D 96 |
| | K 97 | Q 98 | | G 99 | | K 100 | A 101 | A 102 | B 103 | N 104 | | J 105 | J 106 | J 107 |
| D 108 | | A 109 | F 110 | D 111 | L 112 | | F 113 | M 114 | C 115 | | J 116 | | G 117 | A 118 |
| | I 119 | P 120 | | D 121 | D 122 | F 123 | I 124 | H 125 | G 126 | D 127 | | L 128 | | I 129 |
| G 130 | L 131 | D 132 | C 133 | | A 134 | A 135 | H 136 | | B 137 | N 138 | I 139 | | | |

A. Legendary spring of agelessness (3 wds.)
59 135 102 4 109 13 82 56 118 134 58 101 21 15 66

B. Unctuously
38 43 103 55 30 137

C. Customary practice
115 49 79 37 133

D. He usually appears about the 5th inning (2 wds.)
10 108 111 31 127 87 121 35 96 132 11 34 122

E. Uproar
18 68 78 9 42 3

F. 1963 Tommy Roe hit
63 33 123 14 113 16 110 25 77

G. Phoenix suburb (2 wds.)
32 130 74 99 126 71 117 93

H. Certain construction workers
94 125 88 1 91 136 81

I. Convenient
95 124 129 5 72 119 139 84 41

J. Country music and Tennessee capital
52 106 65 105 107 116 23 48 46

K. Adjective for "waterspout spider" (2 wds.)
44 12 76 69 7 100 17 27 36 97 26

L. "______ Honeymoon" (1951 Debbie Reynolds/Carleton Carpenter hit, 2 wds.)
128 22 47 112 60 28 131

M. Poe's raven's quote
80 2 45 70 19 53 114 64 54

N. Welcome rug
104 67 138 92 57 75 61

O. Cut molars
6 73 29 89 62 24

P. Endangered North American stork (2 wds.)
90 120 20 39 51 40 86 85

Q. Four hugs at close of friendly letter
83 98 50 8

## 13 CAN YOU FOLLOW DIRECTIONS?

*Start with the phrase "five barley loaves" at the top and follow the directions, step-by-step. Keep the letters in order at each step, making only the change requested. The final answer will be a phrase that is related to the beginning phrase.*

1. Leave the three words in order and reverse the letters in each individual word.
2. Delete every fourth letter.
3. Beginning at the left, in every group of three letters, switch the first and second letters.
4. Switch the first group of three letters with the second group of three.
5. Delete all O's, I's and L's.
6. Add a T to each end of the row.
7. Add a K after the second letter.
8. Before the last letter, add the first name of Ginger Rogers's second husband.
9. Reverse the order of the first three letters; reverse the order of the last four letters.
10. Change the Y to S and delete the 10th and 11th letters.
11. Switch the first four letters with the last four letters.

FIVEBARLEYLOAVES

1. ____________________
2. ____________________
3. ____________________
4. ____________________
5. ____________________
6. ____________________
7. ____________________
8. ____________________
9. ____________________
10. ____________________
11. ____________________

## 14 ADD-A-LETTER 3

*Begin with the letter shown, then add one letter at each step, rearranging the letters each time to fit the definition at the right. The last answer will be a key word from the book of John.*

| Clue | Answer |
|---|---|
| | A |
| Abbreviated morning | _ _ |
| Scottish headgear | _ _ _ |
| Eve, to Adam | _ _ _ _ |
| Vapor | _ _ _ _ _ |
| Jesus, to the disciples | _ _ _ _ _ _ |

## 15 MIXED BLESSINGS

*Find each two-word phrase below by sorting the letters for each word. The letters of each word are given in the correct order, but the two words have been mixed. For example, "blue moon" could be "B L M U O E O N." Each phrase is from the book of John. A hint, if you need it, has been given for each one.*

1. LIWAVITERNG ________ Better than Dasani
2. FISTRONEST ________ It was never thrown
3. FATAHBREAHARM ________ Patriarchal VIP
4. BMALINND ________ Some think an umpire is one
5. GOSHOEPHDERD ________ Jesus said, "I am the ___ ___"
6. THOWEULVERS ________ Jesus said these were in a day
7. GOWOROKDS ________ Nice, but they won't get you into heaven
8. CHIPERFIESTS ________ One of many Jewish temple occupants
9. MANMANSYIONS ________ Disney has a haunted one
10. TRUVEINE ________ Jesus said, "I am the ___ ___"
11. PURRPOLEBE ________ Kingly garb
12. DOTHUBOMASTING ________ Famous for not believing

## 16 WORD LADDER 2

*Each ladder has five columns. Every answer in column A will have five letters; every answer in column B will have four; answers in column C will have three. After answering the definition for A1, drop one letter and rearrange the remaining four letters to make the answer for B1. Place the dropped letter into the box to the left of column A. Drop another letter from the B1 answer and rearrange the remaining three letters to form the answer for C1. Place the dropped letter into the box to the right of column C. Continue this pattern for the entire puzzle. When finished, the columns of dropped letters, reading down, will reveal a phrase from the book of John.*

| | | A | | | | | B | | | | C | | | |
|---|---|---|---|---|---|---|---|---|---|---|---|---|---|---|
| 1 | | | | | | | | | | | | | | |
| 2 | | | | | | | | | | | | | | |
| 3 | | | | | | | | | | | | | | |
| 4 | | | | | | | | | | | | | | |
| 5 | | | | | | | | | | | | | | |
| 6 | | | | | | | | | | | | | | |

A1. Clan
A2. Square or circle
A3. Celebration
A4. Pointer
A5. "Come on-a My ______"
A6. Fad
A7. Impetuous

B1. Place for a coffin
B2. They come in a pod
B3. Snare
B4. Lion talk
B5. Colors
B6. Door ding
B7. Slangy agreement

C1. "Johnny ______"
C2. Parrot
C3. Average
C4. Paddle
C5. Subjective feminine pronoun
C6. Beginning's opposite
C7. Nautical agreement

## 17 THE WORD WITHIN

*Fill in the blanks with answer words that, when combined with the given letters on each side, will make longer words. No rearranging of letters is necessary. The number of letters in the answer words is given in parentheses for each. When read top to bottom, the completed answer words will reveal a quotation of Jesus from the book of John.*

1. R________________SE (1)
2. N________________E (2)
3. O________________R (3)
4. S________________LY (5)
5. S________________A (2)
6. RA________________R (3)
7. OTHER________________LY (5)

---

## ONE OR THE OTHER 2

*Cross out one letter in each box so that the remaining letters will spell out a quotation from the book of John. A black box signifies the end of a word.*

| F / T | O / H | E / R | ■ | L / S | H / I | G / E | E / H | T / P | ■ | F / S |
|---|---|---|---|---|---|---|---|---|---|---|
| E / O | R / L | L / V | E / O | W / S | ■ | T / H | H / I | M / E | ■ | F / A |
| N / O | R / D | ■ | T / W | R / H | A / E | Y / T | ■ | K / S | T / N | O / E |
| W / M | ■ | T / H | H / I | E / S | ■ | V / L | O / I | G / I | H / C | T / E |

## 19 CHAIN LINKS

*Place the five-letter answer of each clue in the boxes at the right. The answers form a chain: The last letter of each answer is the first letter of the next answer, and the last letter of the last answer is the first letter of the first answer. When all correct answers have been placed, the shaded column, reading top to bottom, will reveal a quotation of Jesus from the book of John.*

1. *Gulliver's Travels* author
2. Pisa leaner
3. Actor Claude of *Casablanca*
4. Bowling mishap
5. Spring bloomer
6. ______ button
7. Influence
8. Venerated emblem
9. Dallas Cowboy Austin
10. Bundle of wheat
11. Superhero Gordon
12. Mayhem
13. Musical volume dir.
14. Burial vault
15. Angels' AL Rookie of the Year 2012
16. Elephant's luggage?
17. Paul Revere hit
18. Indifferent
19. ______ strip
20. Local eateries
21. Shallow
22. Musical direction for slowly
23. Of the eye
24. NFL equines
25. Basketball turnover
26. Will Rogers's prop
27. Desert watering hole

## 20 WORD ADDITION

*Begin with the word in the first column. Add one letter to it and rearrange all of the letters to form a word that answers the clue at the right. Write the additional letter on the first blank and the new word on the second blank. When all of the first-blank correct letters have been filled in, a quotation of Jesus from the book of John will be revealed, reading top to bottom.*

| | | | | | | |
|---|---|---|---|---|---|---|
| 1. | STEAD | + | ____ | = | ____________ | Sewed loosely |
| 2. | TRIPS | + | ____ | = | ____________ | Singular feature of tiger or zebra |
| 3. | LATER | + | ____ | = | ____________ | Vacation cabin or car |
| 4. | URGE | + | ____ | = | ____________ | Reddish cosmetic |
| 5. | REEDS | + | ____ | = | ____________ | Relaxed |
| 6. | REIGN | + | ____ | = | ____________ | One of ten "handy" features |
| 7. | PIERS | + | ____ | = | ____________ | Seek to attain goal |
| 8. | RANTS | + | ____ | = | ____________ | Filter |
| 9. | TINKER | + | ____ | = | ____________ | Trivial item |
| 10. | AFTER | + | ____ | = | ____________ | Isaac's relation to Esau |
| 11. | ENDEAR | + | ____ | = | ____________ | Educated |
| 12. | MOVER | + | ____ | = | ____________ | Delete |
| 13. | TAMER | + | ____ | = | ____________ | Original recording |
| 14. | LIVER | + | ____ | = | ____________ | Color or metal |
| 15. | LATTE | + | ____ | = | ____________ | Medicinal pill |
| 16. | GLEN | + | ____ | = | ____________ | Sudden forward reach |
| 17. | SERIF | + | ____ | = | ____________ | Struggle |
| 18. | FIRE | + | ____ | = | ____________ | Short in duration |
| 19 | PRIME | + | ____ | = | ____________ | Emperor's kingdom |
| 20 | STONE | + | ____ | = | ____________ | Taken illegally |
| 21 | LEAN | + | ____ | = | ____________ | Foreign-born individual |
| 22 | CHAP | + | ____ | = | ____________ | Color or fruit |
| 23 | RISER | + | ____ | = | ____________ | '60s singer Johnny ______ |
| 24 | GRANT | + | ____ | = | ____________ | PG or G |
| 25 | GREATS | + | ____ | = | ____________ | Out of the ordinary |
| 26 | NADIR | + | ____ | = | ____________ | Bold |

## 21 ADD-A-LETTER 4

*Begin with the letter shown, then add one letter at each step, rearranging the letters each time to fit the definition at the right. The last answer will be a key word from the book of John.*

14th letter
Court divider
"______ Angel" (1958 hit song)
To have (Spanish)
Give in
Everlasting

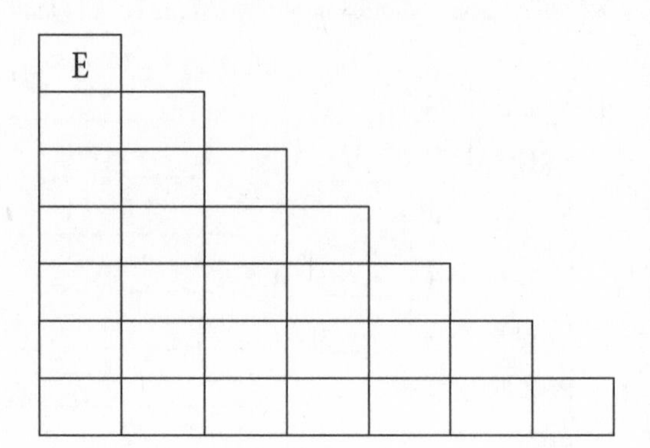


## 22 WRITER'S BLOCKS

*In each row of blocks below is a key word from the book of John, but the word has been divided into blocks of three letters or less and mixed up. The letters within each block are in order, but the blocks are not. Oh, and an extra block of letters has been added for fun. Take away the unneeded block and put the others in order to find 10 key words. A clue has been given to help solve each one.*

| Clue | Blocks | | | | | | Answer |
|---|---|---|---|---|---|---|---|
| 1. Have faith | IE | BEL | VE | RE | | | ______ |
| 2. Everlasting | NAL | ET | HO | ER | | | ______ |
| 3. Third day miracle | TI | AL | SUR | RE | ON | REC | ______ |
| 4. Last Supper | OV | ER | ALE | SS | PA | | ______ |
| 5. Minister | VA | SER | ARE | NT | | | ______ |
| 6. Occupation | PHE | SHE | IAN | RD | | | ______ |
| 7. Anyone | SO | WHO | ER | EV | ENT | | ______ |
| 8. Rabbi | ST | ER | MA | N | | | ______ |
| 9. Holy Spirit | FOR | COM | MA | TER | | | ______ |
| 10. Reverence | IP | WO | MAN | RSH | | | ______ |

## 23 NICODEMUS & JESUS

*John 3 tells of the encounter between Jesus and Nicodemus, who visited Him under cover of darkness, asking questions of eternal significance. Out of this meeting came arguably the most familiar verse in the Bible, John 3:16. See how many of the words and phrases from that famous visit you can find in the grid below. Words may run forward, backward, horizontal, vertical, or diagonal.*

| | | | | | | | | | | | | | | |
|---|---|---|---|---|---|---|---|---|---|---|---|---|---|---|
| S | G | N | I | H | T | Y | L | N | E | V | A | E | H | S |
| M | A | S | T | E | R | J | L | A | L | I | L | V | A | K |
| R | W | N | O | U | S | E | R | I | V | I | O | E | M | I |
| E | H | I | N | E | S | S | A | L | G | I | E | R | O | N |
| H | O | D | A | H | E | U | A | H | T | H | G | I | N | G |
| C | S | N | T | T | N | S | M | R | O | W | T | L | E | D |
| A | O | I | I | E | T | A | I | E | O | A | R | Y | N | O |
| E | E | W | R | V | I | N | E | R | D | G | O | V | I | M |
| T | V | V | I | E | W | A | L | E | A | O | E | E | A | O |
| I | E | R | P | I | P | D | M | O | R | H | C | R | G | F |
| D | R | E | S | L | E | T | R | U | T | H | P | I | A | G |
| N | O | S | N | E | T | T | O | G | E | B | Y | L | N | O |
| E | P | I | B | B | A | R | O | N | A | T | H | Y | R | D |
| R | E | T | A | W | R | E | N | A | M | F | O | N | O | S |
| T | L | E | F | I | L | L | A | N | R | E | T | E | B | S |

Believeth
Born again
Eternal life
Heavenly things
Jesus
Kingdom of God
Light
Master
Nicodemus
Night
Not perish
Only begotten Son
Pharisee
Rabbi
Son of man
Spirit
Teacher
Truth
Verily verily
Water
Whosoever
Wind
Witness
World

## 24 WORD LADDER 3

*Each ladder has five columns. Every answer in column A will have five letters; every answer in column B will have four; answers in column C will have three. After answering the definition for A1, drop one letter and rearrange the remaining four letters to make the answer for B1. Place the dropped letter into the box to the left of column A. Drop another letter from the B1 answer and rearrange the remaining three letters to form the answer for C1. Place the dropped letter into the box to the right of column C. Continue this pattern for the entire puzzle. When finished, the columns of dropped letters, reading down, will reveal a phrase from the book of John.*

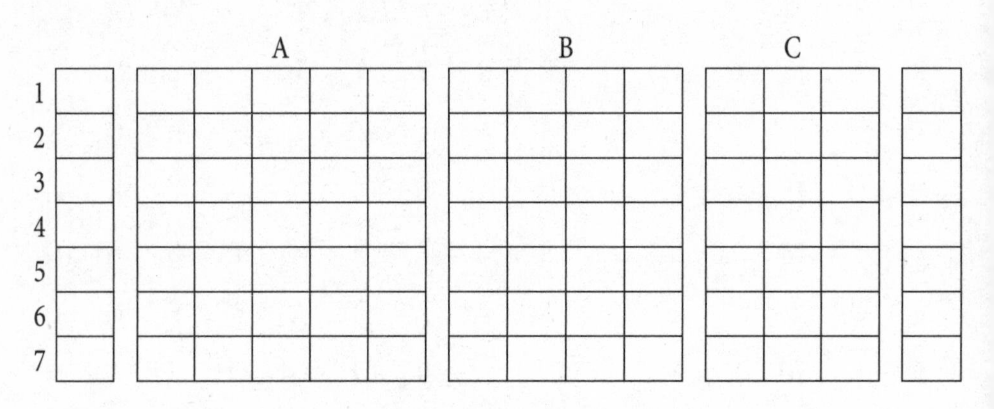

| A | B | C |
|---|---|---|
| A1. Woodworking tool | B1. Back of the neck | C1. It's mightier than the sword |
| A2. Mumble | B2. Pealed | C2. Long, narrow fish |
| A3. Ellipses | B3. And | C3. "My Gal ______" |
| A4. McFadden of *Star Trek* fame | B4. Adult male red deer | C4. Fuel |
| A5. Unwanted house pest | B5. Sear | C5. Part of a circle |
| A6. By no means | B6. Change course | C6. Increase speed |
| A7. Respond | B7. Utility vehicle | C7. Singer Stevens |

## 25 THE FINAL WORD

*Fill in the missing letters to make common three-letter words below. Then transfer those letters to the corresponding numbers in the grid. Be careful; more than one letter will make a complete word, but only one letter will correctly complete the final word in the grid. The final word will be a key word from the book of John.*

| | | | |
|---|---|---|---|
| 1. P___T | 4. CA___ | 7. ___IT | 11. RU___ |
| 2. ___OW | 5. ___AY | 8. A___E | 10. ___OT |
| 3. ___AR | 6. ___CE | 9. M___X | |

| 1 | 2 | 3 | 4 | 5 | 6 | 7 | 8 | 9 | 10 | 11 |
|---|---|---|---|---|---|---|---|---|---|---|
| | | | | | | | | | | |

## 26 ADD-A-LETTER 5

*Begin with the letter shown, then add one letter at each step, rearranging the letters each time to fit the definition at the right. The last answer of each puzzle will be a key word from the book of John.*

Ma's counterpart
Mimic
Peel
Javelin
Scant
Washes again
Last Supper celebration

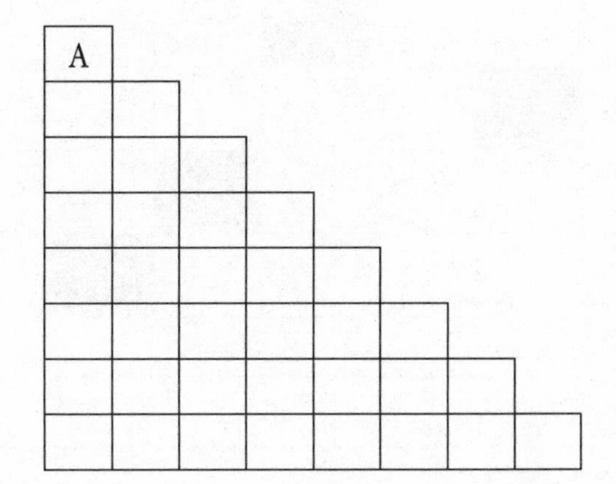

## 27 A PROCESS OF ELIMINATION

*Follow the directions below, eliminating items from the word list. When the correct items have been removed, the remaining words, reading left to right, top to bottom, will reveal a quotation from the book of John.*

1. Delete all words that rhyme with Flynn.
2. Delete all parts of a shoe.
3. Delete all flowers.
4. Delete all words containing three consecutive letters of the alphabet in reverse order.
5. Delete all two-letter state abbreviations.
6. Delete all homonyms of letters of the alphabet.
7. Delete all words that combine with *board* to make a new word.
8. Delete all anagrams of "thrae."

| | | | | | |
|---|---|---|---|---|---|
| In | All | Earth | When | Lilies | Be |
| Things | Are | Were | Heart | Tongue | Head |
| Sole | You | Made | Walk | Room | Rose |
| Me | Fed | Upon | Sin | By | Been |
| Or | See | Him | | | |

_______________________________________________

_______________________________________________

## ONE OR THE OTHER 3

*Cross out one letter in each box so that the remaining letters will spell out a quotation from the book of John. A black box signifies the end of a word.*

| I O | F N | ■ | A M | N A | D Y | ■ | M C | E A | T N |
|---|---|---|---|---|---|---|---|---|---|
| ■ | W S | E H | R E | R V | E T | ■ | M B | E Y | ■ |
| G L | O E | T D | ■ | H W | I A | S M | ■ | S F | E O |
| L N | L D | E O | R W | ■ | B M | E Y | ■ | ■ | ■ |

______________________________________________

______________________________________________

## ADD-A-LETTER 6

*Begin with the letter shown, then add one letter at each step, rearranging the letters each time to fit the definition at the right. The last answer will be a key word from the book of John.*

12th letter
Fib
Tribe of the priesthood
Bile-producing organ
Truly

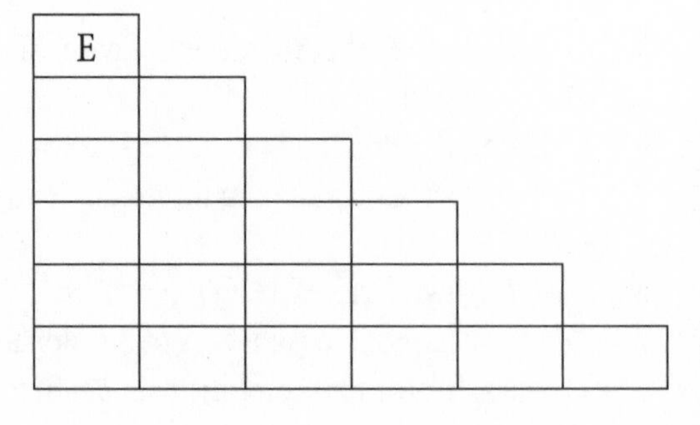

## 30 CROSSROADS

*Each crossroad below contains two words that make a phrase from the book of John. Fill in the blanks from the word list below. The first word of each phrase should be placed down, and the second word across.*

| | | | |
|---|---|---|---|
| Abraham | Father | Mansions | Verily |
| Again | Good | Many | Verily |
| Bear | Great | Multitude | Vine |
| Born | Jesus | Shepherd | Wept |
| Eternal | Life | True | Witness |

1.

2.

3.

4.

5.

6.

7.

8.

9.

10.

## 31 DOUBLE PLAY

*Fill in the blanks for each sentence below with anagrams—one blank will be filled with a word whose letters can then be rearranged to make the second word. Note: the final sentence contains two anagrams.*

1. For his betrayal of Jesus, Judas received a __________ of silver, but he didn't hide it in a __________.
2. Jesus told Peter, "You __________ deny me thrice," before He was led into the __________ of the high priest's house.
3. After the Last Supper, the disciples crossed a sparkling __________ to a garden where their __________ was arrested.
4. The wind may have blown the __________ on the Pharisees' mantles as Jesus wrote on the ground with His __________.
5. The Empire of __________ ruled __________ than just Judea.
6. The thief comes to __________, kill and destroy — at __________ that's what Jesus said.
7. Jesus couldn't __________ weeping when He saw the sadness of Lazarus's __________, Mary.
8. The Jews __________ Jesus heal the man who __________ born blind.
9. Because they __________ Him, the chief priests wanted to put Jesus to __________.
10. After shouting bitter __________, Peter drew his __________ in anger to cut off the servant's ear.
11. Many Jews who __________ in the village were afraid of Jesus' miracles, and insultingly said that He had a __________.
12. The gist of the __________ is that men like __________ better than light; the life they __________ is __________.

## 32 HOW MANY WHAT?

*Fill in the blank following each number below with the name of what's being counted. The first letter of each answer has been given as a hint. The Scripture reference from the book of John is given in parentheses.*

1. After the feeding of the multitude, 12 b__________ of fragments were gathered (6:13).
2. The pool at Bethesda had 5 p__________ (5:2).
3. There were 6 w__________ at the marriage in Cana (2:6).
4. When Mary looked inside of Jesus' tomb, 2 a__________ spoke to her (20:12).
5. Jesus said, "Destroy this temple, and in 3 d__________ I will raise it up (2:19).
6. The man at the pool of Bethesda had been sick for 38 y__________ (5:5).
7. When Jesus asked Philip about feeding the multitude, Philip said that 200 p__________ of bread wasn't enough (6:7).
8. At the marriage in Cana, the waterpots contained 2 or 3 f__________ each (2:6).
9. When Mary anointed the feet of Jesus, Judas thought it was a waste and asked why the ointment had not been sold for 300 p__________, and the money given to the poor (12:5).
10. When 5,000 m__________ were fed, Jesus miraculously used 5 l__________ and 2 f__________ (6:9–10).

## 33 INITIAL CHANGES

*Replace the first letter of each word below to make another word that will complete the verse from the book of John. No letters or words have to be rearranged.*

FOUR BORROW WHALL ME BURNED SNTO BOY

______________________________________________

## 34 RED-LETTER EDITION

*Each answer below is the word that fills in the blank to complete the phrase in the clue. All of the phrases are from sayings of Jesus in the book of John. When each answer is correctly filled in, the shaded boxes, reading down, will reveal a quotation of Jesus that fits the theme of this puzzle. The Scripture reference from John for each clue is given in parentheses.*

1. "Father, ___ thy name" (12:28)
2. "Let not your ___ be troubled (14:27)
3. "Lazarus, ___ forth" (11:43)
4. "Ye shall know the ___" (8:32)
5. "Cast the net on the ___ side" (21:6)
6. "As Moses lifted up the ___" (3:14)
7. "Put up thy ___ into the sheath" (18:11)
8. "___ in me, and I in you" (15:4)
9. "Mine hour is not ___ come" (2:4)
10. "Peace be ___ you" (20:26)
11. "___ do I condemn thee" (8:11)
12. "I am the ___ vine" (15:1)
13. "God is a ___" (4:24)
14. "That ___ joy might be full" (15:11)
15. "Peace I leave with ___" (14:27)
16. "Thy word is ___" (17:17)
17. "Men loved darkness ___ than light" (3:19)
18. "Before Abraham ___, I am" (8:58)
19. "My doctrine is not ___" (7:16)
20. "Lift up your eyes and look on the __" (4:35)
21. "Ye do the deeds of your ___" (8:41)
22. "Wilt thou be made ___" (5:6)
23. "I ___ overcome the world" (16:33)
24. "For God so loved the ___" (3:16)
25. "I have not a ___" (8:49)
26. "I saw thee under the ___ tree" (1:48)
27. "Come and ___" (21:12)

______________________________

______________________________

## 35 LEFTOVERS

*Answer the quiz questions below. The answers may be found in the list of words, though not necessarily in order. Cross off each answer from the list. The remaining words, when read left to right, top to bottom, will reveal a quotation from the book of John. Scripture references have been given at the end of each question.*

| | | | |
|---|---|---|---|
| The | Angel | Peter | Said |
| Your | Word | Truth | Judas |
| Shall | Rise | And | Make |
| Meat | You | Free | Sabbath |

1. What troubled the water at the pool of Bethesda? (5:4)____________________
2. On what day did Jesus heal the blind man? (9:14)____________________
3. "In the beginning was the __________." (1:1)
4. When Jesus stood on the shore of Galilee, what did He ask the disciples (who had been fishing) if they had? (21:5)____________________
5. Which disciple left the Last Supper first? (13:30)____________________
6. Speaking of Lazarus to his saddened sister Martha, Jesus said, "They brother shall __________ again." (11:23)
7. "Thou hast well __________, I have no husband." (4:17)
8. "Lift up __________ eyes and look on the fields." (4:35)
9. "Come __________ dine." (21:12)
10. Which disciple denied knowing Christ three times? (13:38)____________________

________________________________________________________

## 36 LEFT HAND, RIGHT HAND

*Use the letters below to compete a 12-word verse from the book of John. The letters are in the correct order (without the spaces), but are divided into two groups, according to which hand is used to type them on a keyboard. Beginning with the right hand, put the words together again, adding spaces in the proper places, to complete the verse.*

Left Hand

F E W T E S E T G S A A R E E F E D T E

Right Hand

I Y K N O H H I N H P P Y Y I Y O H M

________________________________________________________

## 37 QUOTATION CODES

*Each numbered puzzle below is a quotation from the book of John in code. Each puzzle has its own code: one letter stands for another letter, always the same one within each puzzle. When you have identified a word in the quotation, use the solved letters to help decode other words in the same quotation. For example, KDBBDF could be LETTER.*

1.

G E T F R O M F U N B U M T C H T N E

____ ______ ____ _____ ______

U P M M F T H G U B R P K I N.

____ ______ ______ ___

2.

Q I C T I L D I Z I E W L S A W B I C Z L

____ ____ ___ ______ ____ ______

S A F S A W T F E W A N D I P Z G

_____ ___ _____ ____ _____

O W T I S S W P D I P.

__________ ____

3.

J S B E A N P R O L S K A S M E N

___ _____ __________ ____

P B E A N U S O L S K A S.

__ _____ __________

4.

T O S E R V A N T E J R N W N X

___ _________ ___ ____ ___

W B E J P N G C A.

_____ ______

5.

A R  T O  S O O N  E T  F L E E Z I Q E O I B Y

___ ___ ______ ___ ____________________

T O  Y U Z K K  Z H A Q O  A I  E T  K L W O.

___ ________ ________ ___ ___ ______

6.

S N  D S J D  H L  C H D S P E D  L H O

___ ______ ___ ___________ ____

J Z P O V  M P E,  A N D  S H Z  G H X L D

________ _____ _____ _____ ________

F J L D  J  L D P O N  J D  S N X.

______ __ ________ ___ _____

## 38 MOVIN' UP 2

*Move the letters in each column up and into the boxes above (not necessarily in the order the letters are in now) to find a quote from Jesus in the book of John. A block signifies the end of a word.*

| | | | | | | | | | |
|---|---|---|---|---|---|---|---|---|---|
| | | ■ | | | ■ | | | | |
| | | | | ■ | | | ■ | | |
| ■ | | | | | ■ | | | | |
| ■ | | | | ■ | | | ■ | | |
| ■ | | | | | | | | | |
| ■ | | | | | | | ■ | ■ | ■ |

| | | | | | | | | | |
|---|---|---|---|---|---|---|---|---|---|
| I | A | I | D | C | E | C | H | E | N |
| I | D | N | E | D | I | D | L | E | S |
| | F | O | E | E | I | E | O | M | T |
| | I | R | R | E | Y | N | | M | Y |
| | N | U | S | | | P | | N | Y |
| | W | | Y | | | T | | | |

## 39 ASK ME ANOTHER

*Answer these questions from John by choosing the letter beside the correct answer. When completed, the letters will reveal a quotation of Jesus from the book of John.*

1. When the adulterous woman was brought to Jesus, twice He wrote on the ______.
   T. wall    I. ground    C. table
2. Peter cut off the ear of the high priest's servant, whose name was ______.
   A. Malchus    H. Thomas    N. John
3. When Philip told Nathanael about Jesus, Nathanael asked, "Can any good thing come out of ______?"
   Y. Bethlehem    O. Judea    N. Nazareth
4. After the Last Supper, Jesus washed the disciples' ______.
   W. hands    U. faces    D. feet
5. Not only did the chief priests consult to kill Jesus, but also ______.
   O. John    M. Lazarus    H. Judas
6. The man at the pool of Bethesda had been sick for 38 ______.
   R. months    A. days    Y. years
7. When Mary Magdalene visited the tomb early in the morning, she thought Jesus was ______.
   F. the gardener    D. an angel    S. the centurion
8. Nicodemus came to see Jesus by ______.
   T. the river    A. night    I. ship
9. Jesus said to work while it is day before night comes when no man can ______.
   T. work    S. walk    N. see
10. As Jesus was being tried before the high priest, the disciple who warmed himself outside with the servants was ______.
    A. Thomas    S. Matthew    H. Peter
11. Peter, Andrew, and Philip were from the city of ______.
    L. Jerusalem    E. Bethsaida    A. Capernaum
12. The woman Jesus met at the well was a ______.
    L. Syrian    V. Judean    R. Samaritan
13. When Jesus asked the people why they were trying to kill Him, they said He had a ______.
    I. lot of nerve    A. devil    E. problem

14. When the soldiers put a crown of thorns on Jesus, they also put on him a purple ______.
R. robe F. sash M. tunic

15. Jesus performed His first miracle at a ______.
Y. synagogue E. wedding T. well

16. Although no other Gospel writer recorded it, John wrote about ______.
I. Peter's denial O. turning water into wine A. the anointing of Jesus' feet

17. Peter denied knowing Christ three ______.
N. times U. days M. hours

18. Jesus was asked, "Art thou the King of the Jews?" by ______.
B. Peter E. Pilate G. John's disciples

______________________________________________

______________________________________________

# ANSWERS

# THE GOSPEL ACCORDING TO ST. MATTHEW

## JESUS' GENEALOGY

1. Ruth 2. Jacob (Gen. 35:10) 3. David (1 Sam. 16:23) 4. Rahab [Rachab] (Josh. 2:18) 5. Asa (2 Chron. 16:12–13) 6. Abraham (Gen. 17:4) 7. Joseph (Matt. 1:16) 8. Isaac (Gen. 21:5) 9. Boaz [Booz] (Ruth 4:8–10) 10. Jesse (1 Sam. 16:10–11) 11. Solomon (1 Kings 11:3) 12. Zerubbabel (Hag. 1:14)

## ADD-A-LETTER 1

me, met, teem, meter, temper, tempter

## CAN YOU FOLLOW DIRECTIONS?

JOSEPHLAIDTHEBODYINHISOWNTOMB
1. JOSEPHDIALTHEYDOBINHISOWNBMOT
2. DIALTHEYDOBINHISOWNBMOTHPESOJ
3. DIALDOBINHISOWNBJ
4. SIALSOBINHISOWNBJ
5. SIASIRSLSOBINHISOWNBJ
6. SIASIRSIEHSOBINHISOWNBIEH
7. SIASIRSIEHOFINHISOWNBIEH
8. SIASIRSIEHOFINHISTONBIEH
9. SIASIRSIEHOFINHISTONSIEH
10. SIRSIEHOFINHISTONSIEH
11. SIRSIEHOFERETONSIEH
12. SIRSIEHROFERETONSIEH
13. SIRSIEHROFEREHTONSIEH
14. NESIRSIEHROFEREHTONSIEH
15. HEISNOTHEREFORHEISRISEN (Matt. 28:6)

## KNOCKOUTS

"For the Son of man is come to save that which was lost" (Matt. 18:11).

## THE PARABLE OF THE SOWER

sower, out, sow, by, birds, on, rocky, soil, up, no, sun, risen, root, fell, grew, good, some, times

## MOVIN' UP 1

"Pray to thy Father which is in secret and thy Father which seeth in secret shall reward thee openly" (Matt. 6:6).

## THE WORD WITHIN

1. less 2. re 3. he 4. eek 5. or 6. hey 7. hall 8. her 9. th 10. art

Promise: "Blessed are the meek for they shall inherit the earth." (Matt. 5:5)

## CHANGE-A-LETTER

"Heaven and earth shall pass away, but my words shall not pass away" (Matt. 24:35).

## LEFTOVERS

1. woman 2. hate 3. wedding 4. three 5. money 6. love 7. yes 8. servants 9. teach 10. disciples.
Quotation: "No man can serve two masters" (Matt. 6:24).

## VANITY PLATES

1. f 2. d 3. j 4. g 5. c 6. h 7. a 8. i 9. b 10. e

## ONE OR THE OTHER

"Give us this day our daily bread" (Matt. 6:11).

## CROSSROADS

1. false prophet 2. beloved son 3. five loaves 4. daily bread 5. wise men 6. blind man 7. wicked one 8. kingdom come

## LOST SHEEP

| | | | | | | | | | | | | | | | | | | | |
|---|---|---|---|---|---|---|---|---|---|---|---|---|---|---|---|---|---|---|---|
| S | E | P | E | E | S | H | P | S | S | E | E | H | S | P | H | S | E | E | E |
| P | H | E | E | S | H | E | E | S | P | S | E | H | E | E | S | P | H | P | E |
| E | S | P | P | H | E | E | P | H | E | E | P | E | E | S | H | E | E | E | P |
| E | E | H | S | H | P | S | S | E | E | H | P | E | P | E | E | E | H | S | E |
| P | E | S | E | E | P | H | E | S | E | E | H | P | S | P | E | H | E | E | S |
| E | P | E | P | S | E | E | E | P | H | S | E | S | E | E | S | P | H | H | P |
| S | E | P | E | E | S | H | P | S | S | E | E | H | S | P | H | S | E | E | E |
| S | S | E | H | H | E | E | P | H | E | E | P | E | E | S | H | E | E | E | P |
| H | P | S | H | E | S | E | S | H | P | P | E | E | E | E | H | E | E | P | S |
| E | E | P | S | H | E | P | H | E | E | S | H | S | H | E | P | E | S | H | E |
| P | H | E | E | S | H | E | E | S | P | E | E | H | E | E | S | P | H | P | E |
| H | S | E | E | P | E | P | H | P | E | E | S | H | S | H | E | E | H | E | P |
| E | E | S | H | S | E | H | E | E | S | S | P | E | H | E | P | E | S | S | E |
| E | S | E | P | H | E | E | P | H | E | E | P | E | E | S | H | E | E | E | P |
| P | E | H | S | E | P | S | H | E | E | E | S | H | E | P | P | H | H | E | P |
| S | H | E | P | E | S | E | E | P | H | P | E | E | S | H | E | P | E | E | S |
| S | E | P | E | S | S | E | P | H | E | E | P | H | E | E | P | E | E | S | H |
| H | E | H | P | E | H | S | E | P | S | H | E | E | E | S | H | E | P | P | H |
| E | S | H | S | H | P | S | S | E | E | H | P | E | P | E | E | E | H | S | E |
| P | E | H | S | E | S | H | P | S | S | E | E | H | S | P | H | S | E | E | E |

## IT'S A LIVING

chief priest, Pharisee, merchant, king, fisherman, Sadducee, servant, prophet, publican, husbandman

## MATTHEW'S CHRISTMAS QUIZ

1. g 2. o 3. d 4. w 5. i 6. t 7. h 8. u 9. s
Phrase: "God with us" (Matt. 1:23)

## WORD LADDER 1

A: jaunt, share, stone, cause, haste; B: tuna, rash, note, case, hate; C: nut, has, ten, ace, hat. Phrase: Jesus arose

## MOVIN' UP 2

"A city that is set on an hill cannot be hid" (Matt. 5:14).

## EARLY LIFE OF CHRIST

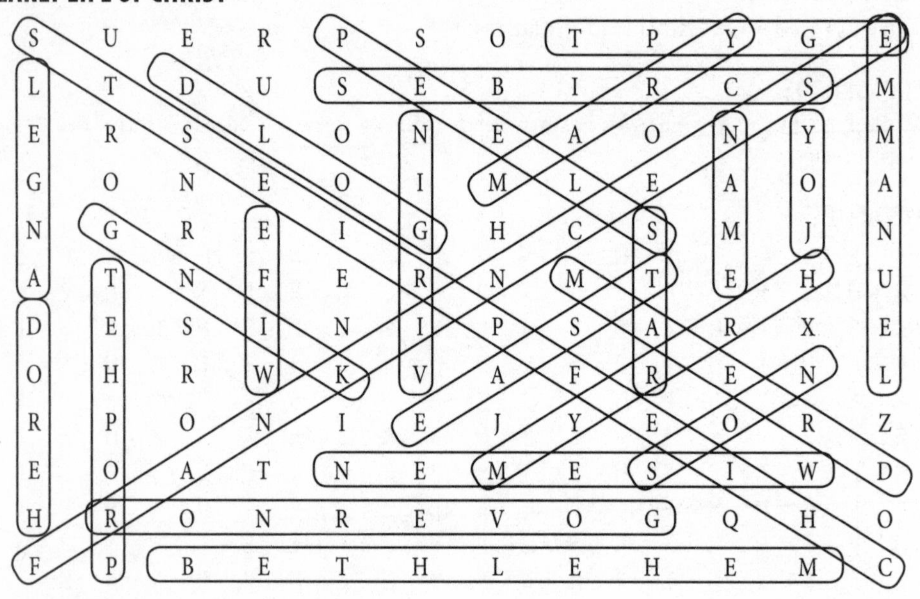


## WHERE AM I?

1. Bethany 2. Bethlehem 3. Bethsaida 4. Canaan 5. Capernaum 6. Egypt 7. Galilee 8. Gethsemane 9. Israel 10. Jericho 11. Jerusalem 12. Nazareth 13. Nineveh 14. Wilderness

## WORD LADDER 2

A: laces, Aaron, demon, water, meant, least, known; B: aces, roan, done, wart, neat, tels, know; C: sea, nor, doe, art, net, set, won. Phrase: Lame man can walk

## MATTHEW'S FAMILIAR PHRASES

five loaves and two fishes; the salt of the earth; many called but few chosen; an eye for an eye; blessed are the meek; the light of the world; rain on the just and the unjust; weeping and gnashing of teeth; a city set on a hill

## FAMOUS PEOPLE WITH BIBLE NAMES

1. Mary 2. Peter 3. Jonas 4. John 5. Simon 6. Martha 7. Joseph 8. Thomas 9. Andrew 10. Caesar 11. David 12. Jesse James

## MOVIN' UP 3

"Whosoever shall compel thee to go a mile, go with him twain" (Matt. 5:41).

## WORD OF MOUTH

1. Herodias (Matt. 14:6) 2. Judas (Matt. 26:47–48) 3. Joseph (Matt. 1:18–19) 4. Woman with blood disease (Matt. 9:20) 5. Peter (Matt. 26:75) 6. Peter's mother-in-law (Matt. 8:14–15) 7. John the Baptist (Matt. 3:4) 8. Pontius Pilate (Matt. 27:22–23) 9. Mary (Matt. 1:20) 10. John (Matt. 20:20–24) 11. Simon of Cyrene (Matt. 27:32) 12. Matthew (Matt. 9:9) 13. Herod (Matt. 2:8) 14. James (Matt. 17:1–5) 15. Joseph of Arimathaea (Matt. 27:57–60)

## PARABLES, PARABLES

1. Fowls 2. Garment 3. Oil 4. Enemy 5. Vineyard 6. City 7. Sun 8. Field 9. Earth 10. Inheritance 11. Net 12. Highways

## WORD TRIANGLES

1. generation 2. repentance 3. bridegroom 4. temptation 5. compassion 6. winebibber 7. wilderness 8. understand 9. boisterous

## WRITER'S BLOCKS

Sadducee, Pharisee, soldier, centurion, shepherd, fisherman, minstrel, moneychanger, publican, governor

## ADD-A-LETTER 2

at, eta, rate, aster, starve, servant

## THE TWELVE

Simon Peter; Andrew; James, the son of Zebedee; John; Philip; Bartholomew; Thomas; Matthew; James, the son of Alphaeus; Thaddaeus; Simon the Canaanite; Judas Iscariot

## A PROCESS OF ELIMINATION

1. one, three, two 2. little, falls, shall, street, will, kill 3. tiny, slight 4. Nazareth, Capernaum, Jerusalem 5. foxes, dove, bear, eagle 6. Angels, Giants 7. know, gnat 8. light, shine, rise 9. heal, steal. Quotation: "… great is your reward in heaven" (5:12).

## WORD LADDER 3

A: latch, tease, paper, elbow, regal, raids; B: chat, seat, reap, bowl, gale, arid; C: cat, sat, rep, bow, lag, air. Phrase: Lepers healed

## SCAVENGER HUNT

1. camel 2. foot 3. leaves 4. coat 5. net 6. fall 7. table 8. kings 9. hearts 10. ruler 11. Charger 12. whole

## ADD-A-LETTER 3

re, per, pert, Peter, repent

## RED LETTER EDITION

1. mustard 2. body 3. lawful 4. desolation 5. power 6. judge 7. destroy 8. treasure 9. faith 10. teach 11. gospel 12. called 13. kingdom 14. yoke 15. thorns 16. prophet 17. bread 18. foxes 19. harmless 20. babes 21. wise 22. shall 23. day. Quotation: "My words shall not pass away" (Matt. 24:35).

## FAMILY TREE

Phrase: Jesus was born the Son of God.

### FIND THE FALSE ONE

1. b 2. a 3. a. 4. c 5. c 6. b 7. b 8. a 9. c 10. b

### SCRAMBLED BEATITUDES

1. Blessed are the poor in spirit: for theirs is the kingdom of heaven. 2. Blessed are they that mourn: for they shall be comforted. 3. Blessed are the meek: for they shall inherit the earth. 4. Blessed are they which do hunger and thirst after righteousness: for they shall be filled. 5. Blessed are the merciful: for they shall obtain mercy. 6. Blessed are the pure in heart: for they shall see God. 7. Blessed are the peacemakers: for they shall be called the children of God. 8. Blessed are they which are persecuted for righteousness' sake: for theirs is the kingdom of heaven.

### HIDDEN ANIMALS

1. **came** later 2. of **ox** 3. **do g**ood 4. competitors **win e**nough 5. **sign at** 6. proto**col t**akes 7. hovere**d over** 8. **tea, Gle**nda 9. Wi-**Fi," she** 10. las**er pen** takes 11. Po**lo, cust**omers 12. hi**m oth**ers 13. **ox, en**joyed 14. ban**shee, p**hantom 15. **chic, Ken**

### SYLLABLE BY SYLLABLE

1. likeness 2. oasis 3. valet 4. Edinburgh 5. yuletide 6. opossum 7. uppermost 8. *Red Witch* 9. Ezra 10. nougat 11. electric 12. Mizzou 13. interior 14. ellipsis 15. sensible 16. Baffin Bay 17. Lake Ontario 18. Esau. Quotation: "Love your enemies; bless them that curse you" (Matt. 5:44).

### THE DISCIPLES

1. Peter (8:14) 2. Andrew (10:2) 3. James and John (10:2) 4. Judas (27:5) 5. Matthew (10:3) 6. James (10:3) [Note: Mark, in his book, mentions that Matthew is the son of Alphaeus.] 7. Peter, James and John (17:1–2) 8. Simon (10:4) 9. Peter (14:29) 10. Judas (10:4) 11. James and John (20:20) 12. Peter (26:69–74) 13. All (10:1) 14. Two disciples of John the Baptist (11:2–3)

## THE GOSPEL ACCORDING TO ST. MARK

### SCAVENGER HUNT

1. mites 2. beat 3. pitcher 4. watch 5. spring 6. lodge 7. shake 8. Cheer 9. charger 10. Angels 11. Colt 12. hands

### MOVIN' UP 1

"If a house be divided against itself, that house cannot stand" (Mark 3:25).

### ADD-A-LETTER 1

an, van, vane, haven, heaven

### LEFTOVERS

1. wine 2. without 3. three 4. fishes 5. work 6. love 7. touch 8. fingers 9. four 10. will. Quotation: "With God, all things are possible" (Mark 10:27).

## A-MAZE-ING QUOTE

"It is easier for a camel to go through the eye of a needle than for a rich man to enter into the kingdom of God" (Mark 10:25).

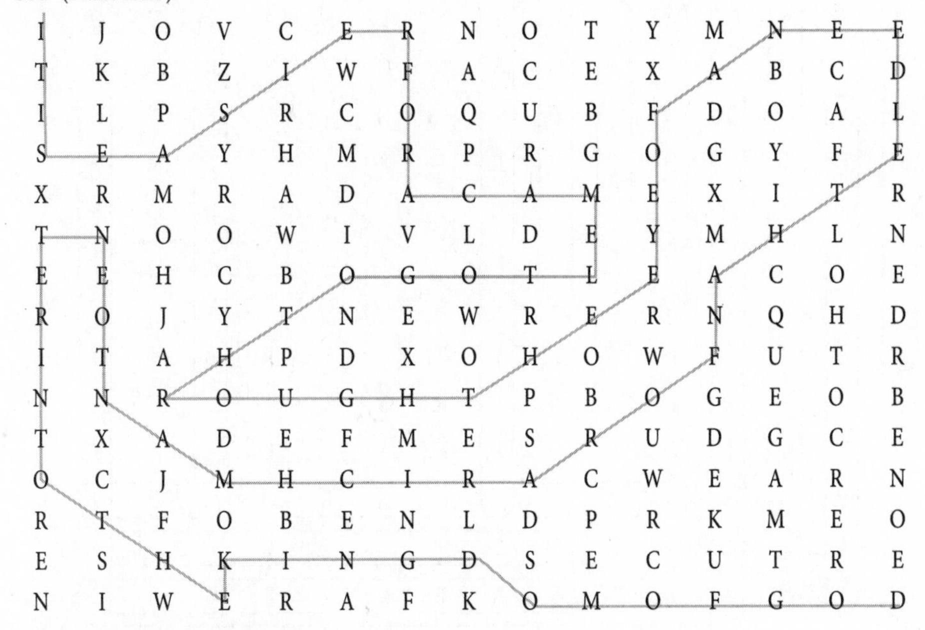

## A PROCESS OF ELIMINATION 1

1. Ravens, Eagles 2. did, eye, noon, ewe 3. dined, find, mind 4. send, ends 5. say, see, can, oh 6. first, deft 7. a, the 8. Pierce, Grant, Bush 9. basket, foot 10. will, trust. Quotation: "Have faith in God" (Mark 11:22).

## WORD LADDER 1

A. garble, tarter, oldies, modest, demean; B. regal, treat, lodes, tomes, named; C. real, Etta, sled, stem, dean. Word: Bridegroom (Mark 2:20)

## MOVIN' UP 2

"What shall a man give in exchange for his soul?" (Mark 8:37).

## LOCATION, LOCATION, LOCATION

1. R 2. O 3. M 4. E 5. I 6. T 7. A 8. L 9. Y. Location: Rome, Italy

## SIGNS OF THE END

G N I M O C T S I R H C D R P
R O A N W H R T I E N A I U Q
F O B S O A O S N G R S B M O
A S O T N T U I G O T L E O N
M E M E D R B R S R I Q T M U
I K I H E E L H O S U U R O S
N A N P R D E C H I S R A W D
E U A O S B S E A G O S Y O E
S Q T R U E D S T N F F A M N
S H I P E G N L R S F A L C E
G T O E O R O A N T A L S E K
N R N S R A W F O S R O M U R
I A P L F N O I T C I L F F A
L E N A F E S R E V I E C E D
L O S F A L L I N G S T A R S

## CHAIN LINKS

1. cable 2. elect 3. talon 4. nails 5. sieve 6. eaves 7. steep 8. Petra 9. ashes 10. steam 11. Magog 12. groom 13. music 14. capes 15. steal 16. lilac. Quotation: "Believe the gospel" (Mark 1:15).

## SYLLABLE BY SYLLABLE

1. Hezekiah 2. Alexandria 3. Volkov 4. epistle 5. satrap 6. accelerate 7. Lydia 8. tunic 9. inheritance 10. Nebo 11. Yukon 12. olive 13. undertow 14. rabbi 15. steadfast 16. Elijah 17. Libya 18. vacation 19. embryo 20. Septuagint 21. Amaziah 22. "Nevermore" 23. dormer. Quotation: "Have salt in yourselves and have peace one with another" (Mark 9:50).

## ADD-A-LETTER 2

or, roe, *Rope*, pre-op, hopper, prophet

## "MARK" MY WORDS

1. mark of the beast 2. Mark Twain 3. question mark 4. hallmark 5. trademark 6. remark 7. postmark 8. Mark Antony 9. flea market 10. marksman 11. telemarketer 12. Denmark. Nickname: "fishers of men"

## WORD LADDER 2

A. drift, harsh, route, sieve, trait, drone, frame; B. dirt, shah, tore, eves, Rita, rend, mare; C. rid, ash, ort, see, tar, red, Ram. Phrase: "Fruit of the vine" (Mark 14:25).

## CHANGE-A-LETTER
"If any man desire to be first, the same shall be last of all and the servant of all" (Mark 9:35).

## MISSING LINKS
1. wilderness (wider) 2. wickedness (swine) 3. generation (green) 4. compassion (camps) 5. understand (trade) 6. possession (pines) 7. discreetly (riled) 8. salutation (slant) 9. earthquake (heart) 10. affliction (cliff)

## THE WORD WITHIN
1. anthem (the) 2. sonnet (son) 3. soft (of) 4. Romans (man) 5. bicameral (came) 6. story (to) 7. given (give) 8. chisel (his) 9. *Lifeboat* (life) 10. ham (a) 11. transom (ransom) 12. formal (for) 13. Germany (many). Quotation: "The son of man came to give his life a ransom for many" (Mark 10:45).

## THE TWELVE DISCIPLES
Thomas, John, Matthew, Thaddaeus, Simon Peter, James, Judas Iscariot, Simon, Philip, Bartholomew, Andrew, James

## ADD-A-LETTER 3
ma, arm, mare, tamer, Master

## CLASSIFIEDS
1. d (10:46) 2. j (1:4–5) 3. c (6:22) 4. f (3:6) 5. b (15:43–46) 6. g (1:19) 7. e (5:22–23) 8. h (15:21) 9. a (2:14) 10. i (5:1–20)

## MISSING PERSONS
1. ninj**a I rus**hed 2. **he rod**e 3. octo**pi later** 4. Oklaho**ma rye** 5. **jam es**pecially 6. **Jose ph**antoms 7. valuab**le violin** 8. **Sal ome**lets 9. fa**thom as** 10. ho**pe Ter**rance

## KNOCKOUTS
"My house shall be called of all nations the house of prayer but you have made it a den of thieves" (Mark 11:17).

## WHO SAID THAT?
1. j 2. b 3. n 4. m 5. e 6. h 7. d 8. l 9. c 10. f 11. k 12. i 13. a 14. g 15. o

## CROSSROADS
1. chief priest 2. rise again 3. money changer 4. burnt offering 5. two mites 6. feast day 7. temple veil 8. forty days

## MOVIN' UP 3
"Whosoever shall receive one of such children in my name receiveth me" (Mark 9:37).

## MIXED BLESSINGS
1. twelve baskets (6:43) 2. holy angels (8:38) 3. good comfort (10:49) 4. uppermost rooms (12:39) 5. poor widow (12:42) 6. sweet spices (16:1) 7. high priest (14:47) 8. white garment (16:5) 9. blind man (10:49) 10. beloved son (9:7)

## ACROSTIC

A. Jethro B. ebbed C. soccer D. unwed E. seethe F. cheated G. *Hotel* H. rime I. inch J. short K. thief. Quotation and speaker: "The stone which the builders rejected is become the head of the corner" —Jesus Christ (Mark 12:10).

## WRITER'S BLOCKS

Jericho, Nazareth, Galilee, Capernaum, Bethsaida, Decapolis, Gethsemane, Bethany, Golgotha, Judea

## ONE AT A TIME

1. stop 2. cash 3. lean 4. spin 5. near 6. mood 7. fire 8. mind 9. drip 10. sale 11. lone 12. went 13. lamp 14. more 15. dare. Answer: their middle name

## MARK'S MALADIES

leprosy, deafness, blindness, issue of blood, smallpox, paralysis, fever, muteness, withered hand, lameness, demon possession, plague

## WORD LADDER 3

A. robed, twine, vinyl, rayon, table, eagle, flash, riper, orate, movie, taped; B. rode, twin, Livy, nary, Abel, glee, lash, pier, rote, move, pate; C. red, wit, Ivy, ran, lea, gel, has, per, rot, Moe, tap. Phrase: "Be not afraid; only believe" (Mark 5:36).

## FILL IN THE BLANK

1. suffer (8:31) 2. the (2:4) 3. little (5:23) 4. children (9:37) 5. to (12:17) 6. come (5:8) 7. unto (1:13) 8. me (2:14) 9. and (14:3) 10. forbid (9:39) 11. them (1:22) 12. not (1:7). Quotation: "Suffer the little children to come unto me and forbid them not" (Mark 10:14).

## ONE OR THE OTHER

"Many that are first shall be last, and the last first" (Mark 10:31).

## MISSING VOWELS

"Take up the cross and follow me" (Mark 10:21).

## PEOPLE AND PLACES

1. Thomas 2. Herodias 3. Yeshua 4. Felix 5. Ananias 6. Isaac 7. Tabitha 8. Hagar 9. Herod 10. Amram 11. Tarsus 12. Horeb 13. Mary 14. Alphaeus 15. Dorcas 16. Eden 17. Timothy 18. Hur 19. Elijah 20. Elisha 21. Wilderness 22. Hophni 23. Onesimus 24. Lazarus 25. Elizabeth. Quotation: "Thy faith hath made thee whole" (Mark 5:34).

## QUOTATION CODE

1. If a kingdom is divided against itself, that kingdom cannot stand (3:24).
2. A prophet is not without honor, but in his own country, and among his own kin, and in his own house (6:4).
3. Whoever will come after me, let him deny himself, and take up his cross, and follow me (8:34).
4. Whoever will save his life shall lose it; but whoever shall lose his life for my sake and the gospel's, the same shall save it (8:35).
5. If you can believe, all things are possible to him that believes (9:23).

### A PROCESS OF ELIMINATION 2

1. Escape, Pilot, Liberty, Accord 2. aid, comfort 3. Paul, John 4. keep, reward, was 5. brook, river 6. by, at, of, from 7. the, see, a 8. seven, king 9. days, week 10. I, his, them. Quotation: "Peace, be still" (Mark 4:39).

### ADD-A-LETTER 4

do, doe, dove, drove, voider, divorce

## THE GOSPEL ACCORDING TO ST. LUKE

### AWAY IN A MANGER

Bethlehem, angels, swaddling clothes, no room in the inn, Joseph, shepherds, night, baby, Mary, peace on earth

### ADD-A-LETTER 1

la, lea, vale, navel, leaven

### MOVIN' UP 1

"Blessed be the Lord God of Israel" (Luke 1:68).

### TAKE-A-LETTER

"Even the very hairs of your head are all numbered" (Luke 12:7).

### ACROSTIC

A. moonroof B. all joy C. Rosh Hashanah D. Yiddish E. thirty-eight F. hither and thither G. eighty-eight H. Mahatma I. Anno Domini J. Grammy nominees K. naughty or nice L. instated M. *Fighting* N. I'm as O. crossed off P. *Arrested Development* Q. tommyrot. Quotation and speaker: "My soul doth magnify the Lord, and my spirit hath rejoiced in God my Savior.... For he that is mighty hath done to me great things; and holy is his name. And his mercy is on them that fear him from generation to generation...." —Mary, The Magnificat (Luke 1:46–50).

### ONE OR THE OTHER 1

"We have done that which was our duty to do" (Luke 17:10).

### ADD-A-LETTER 2

to, rot, torn, toner, cornet, trounce, nocturne, centurion

### THE BARD OR THE BIBLE?

1. *Hamlet* 1.3, 2. Luke 6:35, 3. *Hamlet* 1.3, 4. 1 Cor. 4:3, 5. 1 Cor. 15:55, 6. *Julius Caesar* 2.2, 7. *The Merchant of Venice* 1.3, 8. Both! *The Merchant of Venice* 2.2 and 1 Cor. 15:52, 9. *Romeo and Juliet* 2.3, 10. *King Lear* 1.1, 11. Prov. 10:1, 12. *The Merchant of Venice* 2.2, 13. Prov. 14:13, 14. Prov. 26:5, 15. *Much Ado about Nothing* 3.3

### THE FINAL WORD

1. there 2. share 3. demon 4. lever 5. maker 6. rapid 7. crate 8. strip 9. board 10. tonic. Final word: redemption

## A-MAZE-ING QUOTE

"Give and it shall be given unto you, good measure, pressed down and shaken together and running over" (Luke 6:38).

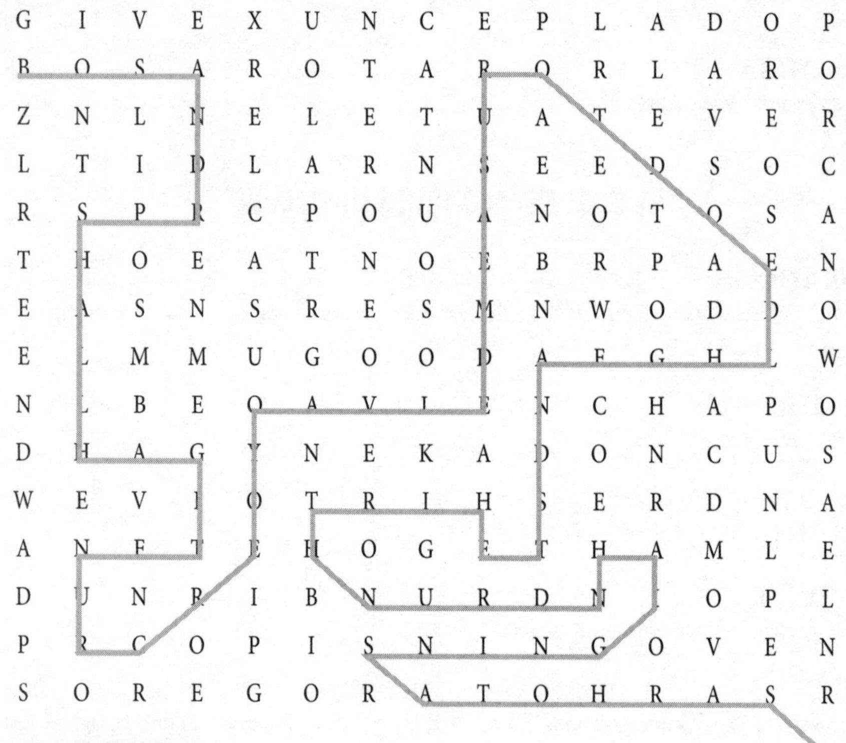

## LUKE'S WHO'S WHO

Magdalene, Herodias, Herod, Theophilus, Mary, Peter, Elisabeth, Levi, Simon, Lazarus, Jairus, Iscariot, Beelzebub, Adam, Martha, Simeon, Moses, Joseph, Joseph, Simon, Pilate, Gabriel, Zebedee. Quotation: "God hath visited his people" (Luke 7:16).

## WORD LADDER 1

A. waste, flier, Tiber, niche, edict, shale, heart, waits, hiker, endue, Endor; B. stew, life, Brit, chin, cite, Leah, rate, wits, heir, dune, rode; C. set, elf, rib, *Inc.*, ice, lea, art, sit, her, due, ore. Phrase: "… a reed shaken with the wind" (Luke 7:24).

## A PROCESS OF ELIMINATION

1. knock 2. from, over, to, upon 3. Rome, Jerusalem, Bethlehem 4. house, temple 5. crimson, rose, maroon 6. stop, field 7. son, father 8. Job, Ruth, Numbers, Judges 9. are, be, see, you 10. lead, silver. Quotation: "Consider the lilies how they grow" (Luke 12:27).

## THE BAPTIZER

John, filled with Holy Ghost, birth foretold, prepared the way, preacher, wilderness, son of Zacharias, Jordan River, prophet, prisoner

## GET OUT OF HERE!

1. Simeon (2:15–16) 2. Shepherds (2:22–38) 3. Barnabas (5:1–11) 4. Mary (8:22–25) 5. Elisha (9:28–36) 6. Mother (15:11–32) 7. Pilate (22:1–38) 8. Paul (22:63–23:25) 9. John the Baptist (23:26–49) 10. Zacchaeus (23:50–24:12)

## ADD-A-LETTER 3

in, gin, grin, reign, fringe, foreign, forgiven

## MOVIN' UP 2

"All flesh shall see the salvation of God" (Luke 3:6).

## HOLEY QUOTATIONS

1. "And thou shalt have joy and gladness; and many shall rejoice at his birth" (Gabriel, 1:14). 2. "Jerusalem shall be trodden down of the Gentiles" (Jesus, 21:24). 3. "Behold the handmaid of the Lord; be it unto me according to thy word" (Mary, 1:38). 4. "Depart from me; for I am a sinful man, O Lord (Simon Peter, 5:8). 5. "Lord, dost thou not care that my sister hath left me to serve alone? (Martha, 10:40). 6. "Mine eyes have seen thy salvation" (Simeon, 2:30). 7. "Art thou only a stranger in Jerusalem, and hast not known the things which are come to pass there in these days?" (Cleopas, 24:18). 8. "Blessed art thou among women, and blessed is the fruit of thy womb" (Elisabeth, 1:42). 9. "If thou be the Son of God, command this stone that it be made bread" (Satan, 4:3). 10. "John have I beheaded: but who is this, of whom I hear such things?" (Herod, 9:9)

## THE STUFF PARABLES ARE MADE OF

| I | P | E | E | H | S | H | I | G | H | W | A | Y | S | P |
|---|---|---|---|---|---|---|---|---|---|---|---|---|---|---|
| B | N | G | R | E | A | T | S | U | P | P | E | R | E | R |
| D | M | U | S | T | A | R | D | S | E | E | D | T | E | O |
| R | N | F | A | T | T | E | D | C | A | L | F | N | R | D |
| A | M | U | C | H | E | L | D | N | A | C | I | U | T | I |
| W | I | D | O | W | N | V | O | O | T | W | N | O | G | G |
| E | D | R | K | R | O | E | L | S | S | A | I | C | I | A |
| T | N | C | A | N | G | E | L | S | T | I | U | R | F | L |
| S | O | B | S | E | G | D | E | H | A | C | T | A | N | S |
| R | I | A | E | H | T | F | O | S | L | W | O | F | C | O |
| A | N | A | M | H | C | I | R | O | B | H | G | I | E | N |
| N | O | B | L | E | M | A | N | E | G | D | U | J | N | A |
| T | R | O | X | E | N | I | W | D | N | A | L | I | O | N |

## THE BIRTH OF JOHN THE BAPTIST

1. W (1:5) 2. I (1:5) 3. L (1:5) 4. D (1:9) 5. E (1:11) 6. R (1:13) 7. N (1:15) 8. E (1:20) 9. S (1:19) 10. S (1:24) 11. V (1:27–36) 12. O (1:56) 13. I (1:59) 14. C (1:63) 15. E (1:64). Phrase: "Wilderness voice"

## QUOTATION CODES

1. Unto him that smiteth thee on the one cheek, offer also the other (6:29).
2. The laborer is worthy of his hire (10:7).
3. The life is more than meat and the body is more than raiment (12:23).
4. The harvest truly is great, but the laborers are few (10:2).
5. Ask and it shall be given you, seek and ye shall find, knock and it shall be opened unto you (11:9).

## LOST COIN

| | | | | | | | | | | | | | | |
|---|---|---|---|---|---|---|---|---|---|---|---|---|---|---|
| O | I | N | C | I | N | I | C | O | N | I | O | N | O | C |
| I | N | O | C | O | I | M | I | C | O | N | N | I | C | O |
| I | O | N | O | O | N | C | O | N | I | C | O | L | N | I |
| N | I | O | O | I | I | O | C | O | N | I | C | O | I | M |
| C | C | I | C | O | N | O | I | O | I | C | M | O | I | C |
| O | I | N | O | I | C | O | I | O | N | O | O | I | N | I |
| I | N | O | M | I | O | C | N | N | O | I | N | I | O | N |
| O | N | I | O | N | C | I | O | N | C | M | O | I | L | C |
| N | O | I | C | O | I | C | I | N | O | C | O | N | I | C |
| C | N | I | O | N | I | C | C | O | I | C | N | C | O | N |
| O | C | I | C | O | N | I | O | N | C | I | O | N | O | C |
| N | I | C | O | N | I | C | O | O | N | C | O | I | C | N |
| I | N | N | C | I | O | N | C | C | O | N | I | O | M | O |
| C | I | C | O | N | O | C | I | O | N | N | M | I | O | C |
| I | O | N | C | N | O | I | C | C | I | O | N | N | I | I |

## WORD ADDITION

1. priest 2. ashes 3. remain 4. chosen 5. repay 6. beast 7. peace 8. after 9. about 10. eternal 11. harvest 12. certain 13. sister 14. earth 15. Stood 16. house 17. Super 18. enter. Quotation: "Peace be to this house" (Luke 10:5).

## ADD-A-LETTER 4

pa, ape, pear, drape, spared, despair, paradise

## MOVIN' UP 3

"What is a man advantaged if he gain the whole world and lose himself" (Luke 9:25).

## RED LETTER EDITION

heal, into, shall, where, obtain, render, desired, without, always, Siloam, which, inward, tempt, house, parables, other, whole, every, righteous. Quotation: "His word was with power" (Luke 4:32).

## WORD LADDER 2

A. upper, diner, taste, Marco, delay, robot, elude; B. pure, rind, test, roam, *Lady*, root, duel; C. per, rid, set, mar, lad, rot, led. Phrase: "Peace be unto you" (Luke 24:36).

## INITIAL CHANGES

"Man shall not live by bread alone" (Luke 4:4).

## SCAVENGER HUNT

1. Ravens 2. *Jeopardy* 3. den 4. net 5. fingers 6. lightning 7. feet 8. FOX 9. bill 10. enter 11. couch 12. needle 13. Anna 14. Time 15. flame 16. calf 17. olives 18. spare 19. serve 20. ring

## THE LAST SUPPER

Passover, Upper Room, thirteen men, cup, fruit of the vine, unleavened bread, two swords, pitcher of water, thanksgiving, "This do in remembrance of me"

## ONE OR THE OTHER 2

"The light of the body is the eye" (Luke 11:34).

## LEFT HAND, RIGHT HAND

"They that are whole need not a physician, but they that are sick" (Luke 5:31).

## WORD LADDER 3

A. relay, route, meats, easel, whims, fiber, defer, regal; B. Yale, tour, east, seal, wish, fire, Fred, gale; C. aye, rut, sea, lea, his, ref, red, lag. Phrase: "Remember Lot's wife" (Luke 17:32).

## SHADY COLUMNS

1. eyelet 2. hearth 3. banana 4. orphan 5. jetsam 6. Mothra 7. afghan 8. Smokey 9. porous 10. grow up 11. Medusa 12. evader 13. Father 14. Sluggo 15. furrow 16. Festus. Quotation: "Ye are of more value than many sparrows" (Luke 12:7).

## SIGNS OF THE SECOND COMING

war, earthquakes, famine, pestilence, family betrayals, armies in Jerusalem, days of vengeance, distress of nations, roaring sea, signs in the sun and moon

## LEFTOVERS

1. centurion 2. send 3. temple 4. this 5. angel 6. tempt 7. where 8. two 9. give 10. is 11. an 12. the. Quotation: "Love your enemies" (6:27).

## KNOCKOUTS

"Thou art my beloved Son; in thee I am well pleased" (Luke 3:22).

### SIX BY SIX

1. loosed 2. loaves 3. leaped 4. follow 5. twelve 6. temple 7. leaven 8. wisdom 9. lilies

### SYLLABLE BY SYLLABLE

1. Houdini 2. Elias 3. trivial 4. homage 5. Aquila 6. Thessalonians 7. Iscariot 8. Sinai 9. Florida Keys 10. Arabian Gulf 11. Indiana 12. Tivoli 13. Hamlet 14. front porch 15. unbelief 16. lulu 17. initial 18. Nana 19. Teapot Dome Scandal 20. Harry James 21. allegro 22. tutti-frutti 23. *Wagon Train* 24. Hoover Dam 25. impromptu 26. cul-de-sac 27. Hezekiah. Quotation: "He that is faithful in that which is least is faithful also in much" (Luke 16:10).

### ONE OR THE OTHER 3

"The kingdom of God is within you" (Luke 17:21).

## THE GOSPEL ACCORDING TO ST. JOHN

### SCAVENGER HUNT

1. clay 2. band 3. *Glory* 4. Glad 5. eyes 6. resort 7. letters 8. Proverbs 9. palm 10. body 11. Miracles 12. branch 13. record 14. draw 15. comforter 16. folk 17. love 18. Marvel 19. present 20. shipping

### WORD LADDER 1

A. gates, opera, solid, raise, stain, bloat; B. seat, reap, Lois, ears, Tina, blot; C. ate, are, Sol, Sea, tan, lob. Phrase: "God is a spirit" (John 4:24).

### ADD-A-LETTER 1

Ma, mar, Rams, roams, Romans

### JOHN WHO?

1. d 2. j 3. i 4. p 5. b 6. h 7. k 8. g 9. a 10. s 11. o 12. n 13. e 14. m 15. t 16. r 17. f 18. q 19. l 20. c

### SHADY COLUMNS

1. wisdom 2. effigy 3. mystic 4. Texaco 5. slalom 6. Folsom 7. Ivanka 8. Lemmon 9. imbued 10. vellum 11. Skokie 12. reason 13. Kermit 14. *Sports*. Quotation: "If ye love me, keep my commandments" (John 14:15).

### ADD-A-LETTER 2

is, sir, stir, trips, Spirit

## A-MAZE-ING QUOTE

"I give unto them eternal life and they shall never perish neither shall any man pluck them out of my hand" (John 10:28).

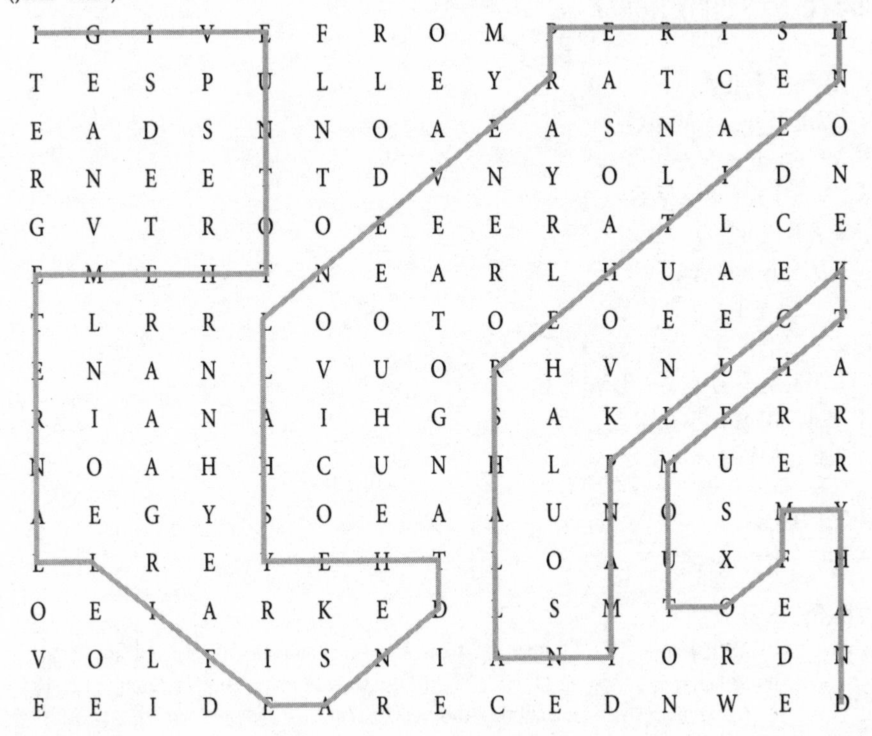

## KNOCKOUTS

1. "I am the true vine ..." (15:1) 2. "... he is a liar and the father of it" (8:44) 3. "... It is I; be not afraid" (6:20) 4. "... Ye must be born again" (3:7) 5. "... If any man thirst, let him come unto me and drink" (7:37)

## ONE OR THE OTHER 1

"If this man were not of God, he could do nothing" (John 9:33).

## SYLLABLE BY SYLLABLE

1. William Tell 2. appetite 3. likeness 4. kismet 5. "Wanted" 6. Havana 7. indoor 8. "Limbo Rock" 9. evergreen 10. Yellowstone 11. edelweiss 12. Harry Lillis 13. *Almanac* 14. volcano 15. eardrum 16. *Twilight Zone* 17. Honolulu 18. envelop 19. largo 20. indignation 21. Goosey Loosey 22. hitherto 23. Timbuktu. Quotation: "... Walk while ye have the light lest darkness come upon you ..." (John 12:35).

## MOVIN' UP 1

"If ye shall ask anything in my name, I will do it" (John 14:14).

## ACROSTIC

A. Fountain of Youth B. oilily C. usage D. relief pitcher E. tumult F. "Everybody" G. El Mirage H. nailers I. opportune J. Nashville K. eensy-weensy L. "Aba Daba" M. "Nevermore" N. doormat O. teethe P. wood ibis Q. OOOO. Quotation and location: "Let not your heart be troubled: ye believe in God, believe also in me. In my Father's house are many mansions: if it were not so, I would have told you. I go to prepare a place for you." ("fourteen, one and two")

## CAN YOU FOLLOW DIRECTIONS?

F I V E B A R L E Y L O A V E S
1. E V I F Y E L R A B S E V A O L
2. E V I Y E L A B S V A O
3. V E I E Y L B A S A V O
4. E Y L V E I B A S A V O
5. E Y V E B A S A V
6. T E Y V E B A S A V T
7. T E K Y V E B A S A V T
8. T E K Y V E B A S A V L E W T
9. K E T Y V E B A S A V T W E L
10. K E T S V E B A S T W E L
11. T W E L V E B A S K E T S

## ADD-A-LETTER 3

a.m., tam, mate, steam, master

## MIXED BLESSINGS

1. living water (4:10) 2. first stone (8:7) 3. Father Abraham (8:39) 4. blind man (9:1) 5. good shepherd (10:11) 6. twelve hours (11:9) 7. good works (10:32) 8. chief priests (11:47) 9. many mansions (14:2) 10. true vine (15:1) 11. purple robe (19:2) 12. Doubting Thomas (20:27)

## WORD LADDER 2

A. tribe, shape, party, arrow, House, trend, heady; B. bier, peas, trap, roar, hues, dent, yeah; C. Reb, ape, par, oar, she, end, aye. Phrase: "Thy word is truth" (John 17:17).

## THE WORD WITHIN

1. I 2. am 3. the 4. light 5. of 6. the 7. world (John 8:12)

## ONE OR THE OTHER 2

"… the sheep follow him for they know his voice" (John 10:4).

## CHAIN LINKS

1. Swift 2. tower 3. Rains 4. split 5. tulip 6. panic 7. clout 8. totem 9. Miles 10. sheaf 11. Flash 12. havoc 13. cresc. 14. crypt 15. Trout 16. trunk 17. "Kicks" 18. stoic 19. comic 20. cafes 21. shoal 22. largo 23. optic 24. Colts 25. steal 26. lasso 27. oasis. Quotation: "I will not leave you comfortless…" (John 14:18).

## WORD ADDITION

1. basted 2. stripe 3. rental 4. rouge 5. rested 6. finger 7. aspire 8. strain 9. trinket 10. father 11. learned 12. remove 13. master 14. silver 15. tablet 16. lunge 17. strife 18. brief 19. empire 20. stolen 21. alien 22. peach 23. Rivers 24. rating 25. strange 26. daring. Quotation: "… be not faithless but believing" (John 20:27).

## ADD-A-LETTER 4

en, net, Teen, tener, relent, eternal

## WRITER'S BLOCKS

1. believe 2. eternal 3. resurrection 4. Passover 5. servant 6. shepherd 7. whosoever 8. master 9. comforter 10. worship

## NICODEMUS AND JESUS

S G N I H T Y L N E V A E H S
M A S T E R J L A L I L V A K
R W N O U S E R I V I O E M I
E H I N E S S A L G I E R O N
H O D A H E U A H T H G I N G
C S N T T N S M R O W T L E D
A O I I E T A I E O A R Y N O
E E W R V I N E R D G O V I M
T V V I E W A L E A O E E A O
I E R P I P D M O R H C R G F
D R E S L E T R U T H P I A G
N O S N E T T O G E B Y L N O
I P I B B A R O N A T H Y R D
R E T A W R E N A M F O N O S
T L E F I L L A N R E T E B S

## WORD LADDER 3

A. plane, groan, ovals, Gates, roach, never, react; B. nape, rang, also, stag, char, veer, cart; C. pen, gar, Sal, gas, arc, rev, Cat. Phrase: "Love one another" (John 15:17).

## THE FINAL WORD

1. pet 2. vow 3. ear 4. car 5. lay 6. ace 7. sit 8. ate 9. mix 10. not 11. rug. Final word: everlasting

## ADD-A-LETTER 5

pa, ape, pare, spear, sparse, resoaps, Passover

## A PROCESS OF ELIMINATION

1. when, sin, been 2. tongue, sole 3. lilies, rose 4. fed, upon 5. IN, ME, OR 6. be, are, you, see 7. head, walk, room 8. earth, heart. Quotation: "All things were made by him…" (John 1:3).

## ONE OR THE OTHER 3

"If any man serve me, let him follow me …" (John 12:26).

## ADD-A-LETTER 6

el, lie, Levi, liver, verily

## CROSSROADS

1. great multitude 2. bear witness 3. Jesus wept 4. many mansions 5. true vine 6. born again 7. verily verily 8. eternal life 9. good shepherd 10. Father Abraham

## DOUBLE PLAY

1. reward, drawer 2. shall, halls 3. stream, master 4. fringe, finger 5. Rome, more 6. steal, least 7. resist, sister 8. saw, was 9. hated, death 10. words, sword 11. lived, devil 12. thing, night, live, evil

## HOW MANY WHAT?

1. baskets 2. porches 3. waterpots 4. angels 5. days 6. years 7. pennyworth 8. firkins 9. pence 10. men, loaves, fishes

## INITIAL CHANGES

"... your sorrow shall be turned into joy" (John 16:20).

## RED LETTER EDITION

1. glorify 2. heart 3. come 4. truth 5. right 6. serpent 7. sword 8. Abide 9. yet 10. unto 11. Neither 12. true 13. spirit 14. your 15. you 16. truth 17. rather 18. was 19. mine 20. fields 21. father 22. whole 23. have 24. world 25. devil 26. fig 27. dine. Quotation: "... I am the way, the truth, and the life ..." (John 14:6).

## LEFTOVERS

1. angel 2. Sabbath 3. Word 4. meat 5. Judas 6. rise 7. said 8. your 9. and 10. Peter. Quotation: "... the truth shall make you free" (John 8:32).

## LEFT HAND, RIGHT HAND

"If ye know these things, happy are ye if ye do them" (John 13:17).

## QUOTATION CODES

1. "The Word was made flesh and dwelt among us ..." (1:14).
2. "For God so loved the world that he gave his only begotten son ..." (3:16).
3. "He must increase, but I must decrease" (3:30).
4. "... my kingdom is not of this world ..." (18:36).
5. "If ye keep my commandments, ye shall abide in my love ..." (15:10).
6. "... He that is without sin among you, let him first cast a stone at her" (8:7).

## MOVIN' UP 2

"... If ye continue in my word, then are ye my disciples indeed" (John 8:31).

## ASK ME ANOTHER

1. I (8:8) 2. A (18:10) 3. N (1:46) 4. D (13:5) 5. M (12:10) 6. Y (5:5) 7. F (20:15) 8. A (3:2) 9. T (9:4) 10. H (18:18) 11. E (1:44) 12. R (4:7) 13. A (7:20) 14. R (19:2) 15. E (2:1). 16. O (2:9) 17. N (13:38) 18. E (18:33) Quotation: "I and my Father are one" (John 10:30).